MILTON CANIFF

FOUR COMPLETE STEVE CANYON ADVENTURES

DAMMA EXILE

KITCHEN SINK PRESS

PRINCETON WISCONSIN

ISBN 0-87816-061-2

Library of Congress Cataloging-in-Publication Data

Caniff, Milton, 1907 -
     Damma exile : four complete Steve Canyon adventures / by Milton Caniff
         p.   cm.
     ISBN 0-87816-061-2 (s.c.) : $18.95
     PN6727.C3D3   1991
     741.5'973--dc20   91-16568
                                                        CIP

Publisher: Denis Kitchen. Editor/Art Director: Peter Poplaski. Production assistants: Christi Scholl and Scott Friend. Caniff studio manager: Willie Tuck. Ohio State University, Milton Caniff Research Center: Lucy Caswell.

"Damma Exile" has been a long time coming due to inadequate proofsheets available to us. Thanks to the loan of proofsheets from Editrice Comic Art of Rome, Italy, this volume is finally complete and in your hands. *Mille Grazie, Roma.*

Kitchen Sink Press has collected all of Miton Caniff's *Steve Canyon* from its beginning in 1947. Back issues are available. For information and a free catalog listing all our books, comics and other merchandise, send a card to Kitchen Sink Press, No. 2 Swamp Rd., Princeton WI 54968.

The female character introduced to readers of *Steve Canyon* in 1956 was a perky orphan from Texas, a shirt-tail relative of the hero named Poteet. Milton Caniff, always conscious of trends in public taste, had added another ingredient to his novelistic comic strip.

He decided against using a boy character, probably because a male would have made *Steve Canyon* too similar to his previous strips, *Terry and the Pirates* and *Dickie Dare.* Caniff was also aware of the success and popularity of Harold Gray's *Little Orphan Annie* and the fact that romantic strips like *The Heart of Juliet Jones* and *On Stage* consistently came in near the top of newspaper readership surveys.

And Caniff, approaching his 25th year as a syndicated cartoonist, was an old hand in the romance department. He had enjoyed writing April Kane, the character in *Terry* based on Scarlett O'Hara, and who Poteet resembles in personality. He had maintained decades-long subplots in *Terry* and *Steve Canyon* involving the thwarted love lives of his two leading adult male characters, Pat Ryan and Steve Canyon.

So in 1956, the focus of *Steve Canyon* changes, and we find Canyon missing from the strip for great amounts of time as Caniff tells Poteet's story. The political climate of the day also had something to do with Caniff's decision. The Cold War was at its most frigid, and Caniff was always fond of dropping a boy-meets-girl (or vice versa) story in the midst of a crisis. He was beginning to use the strip to tell the public "why we fight." With Poteet on board, Caniff could contrast action storylines with intimate small town vignettes. With Russia and the United States pointing atomic weapons at each other, Caniff's message was easily understood. Why does Steve Canyon stay in uniform when he could be a movie star (an ultimate American fantasy)? So America can be ready to protect *all* its freedoms, especially small town basketball or "crazy" boy friends (modeled after *Mad* magazine's Alfred E. Newman). This contrasting will be one of Caniff's prominent motifs for the remaining thirty years of the strip.

--Peter Poplaski

DECISION

NOVEMBER 29 to DECEMBER 30, 1956

... AND SO STEVE SEES THE FINISHED RELEASE OF THE PICTURE IN WHICH HE 'ACTED'... OF COURSE POTEET KNOWS NOTHING OF THIS CHAPTER IN HIS LIFE

COUSIN STEVIE B., YOU HAVEN'T SAID A WORD! WERE YOU AS DOWNRIGHT THRILLED AS I AM OVER THAT MOVIE SHOW?

HMM — OH, YES! THAT IS — I — AH — WELL..

...OH, IF I COULD LOOK LIKE THAT SAVANNAH GAY I JUS' WOULDN'T EVEN SPEAK TO PEOPLE!

SHE IS POSITIVELY THE FINAL, ACTUAL, TOTAL LIVING END? DIDN'T YOU THINK SO?

HMM? — OH, YES!

SHUCKS, COUSIN STEVIE B., I'LL BET YOUR MIND IS ON SOME OL' JET ENGINE INSTEAD OF MISS GAY! I'LL GO QUIETLY AN' DREAM ABOUT HER AN' MR. SHEFFIELD! G'NIGHT!

YES-S-S-MY MIND IS ON A JET BOMBER AT THAT! GOOD NIGHT!

COLONEL CANYON, YOU HAD A CALL FROM A MR. SLOANE IN HOLLYWOOD, CALIFORNIA. YOU'RE TO CALL HIM COLLECT...

...HE SAID YOU AND HE FOUGHT TOGETHER AT THE BATTLE OF SAVANNAH

12-2

WELL, POTEET, DID YOU ENJOY THE 'SCARLET PRINCESS'?

GREAT GLORY BE, YES, MRS. TORR! IF I LOOKED LIKE MISS SAVANNAH GAY I WOULDN'T BE ABLE TO PUT DOWN THE MIRROR!

AND AS FOR MR. HUNTLEY SHEFFIELD — WELL, I SWEAR THERE JUST ISN'T ANYONE WHO ACTS LIKE THAT IN THE ENTIRE WORLD!...

...DID COLONEL CANYON HAVE FUN?

HE SEEMED A LITTLE NERVOUS THROUGH THE PICTURE! I RECKON HE HAD SOMETHIN' ON HIS MIND!

MEANWHILE

COLONEL CANYON, YOU WERE TO CALL THE LOS ANGELES OPERATOR! WOULD YOU LIKE ME TO GET HER ON THIS WIRE?

NO. PROBABLY JUST SOME TELEPHONE PRANKSTER FRIENDS OF MINE ON A PARTY! I'M GOING TO HIT THE SACK—I'M EXPECTING TO HAVE SOME INTERESTING DREAMS!

OPERATOR, I DON'T KNOW WHY COL. CANYON DIDN'T CALL YOU BACK LAST NIGHT...

HE'S FLYING RIGHT NOW... YES, I'LL GIVE HIM THE MESSAGE!

POTEET, IF YOU SEE COL. CANYON BEFORE I DO, WILL YOU TELL HIM TO CALL OPERATOR 27 IN LOS ANGELES?

PROBABLY ONE OF HIS HOLLYWOOD GIRL FRIENDS GETTING LONESOME TO SEE HIM!

HI, POTEET! WHAT'S BEEN GOING ON DOWN HERE WHILE I WAS UP EARNING MY FLIGHT PAY?

WHY-AH-NOTHIN', COUSIN STEVIE B., JUS' PLAIN OL' NOTHIN'!

11

12

13

HEY! ARE YOU STILL THERE?

TRYING TO MAKE UP MY MIND WHETHER TO THANK YOU OR LAUGH IN YOUR EAR!

I KNOW ROUGHLY HOW MUCH PAY YOU DRAW IN THE BIRD BUSINESS...

WHY DON'T YOU GRAB SOME EASY PICTURE LOOT WHILE YOU'RE STILL STRONG ENOUGH TO CARRY IT AWAY!

BETTER HURRY BEFORE TELEVISION TAKES OVER THE MOVIE INDUSTRY AND WE'LL ALL BE GIVEN SCREEN TESTS OPENING ICEBOX DOORS!

NO RUSH ON YOUR DECISION! I WON'T CALL YOU BACK BEFORE TEN MINUTES FROM NOW!

SLOANE, I'M NOT EVEN CERTAIN HOW MUCH LEAVE I'VE GOT COMING....

WHEN I TELL YOU THE SALARY MY AGENT IS GOING TO ASK FOR YOU, YOU'LL GET LEAVE!.. WHAT DO YOU SAY TO ---

STUDIO 4

...AND THAT'S PER WEEK, NOT PER YEAR!

— I'VE GOT LEAVE!

12-9

STEVE, WELCOME TO LOTUS LAND!

WHAT, NO DANCING GIRLS? SLOANE, YOU BROUGHT ME OUT HERE UNDER FALSE PRETENSES!

NOT AT ALL! WE'LL HAVE LUNCH AT A DRIVE-IN! THE CAR HOPS ARE AUDITIONING FOR PICTURES EVERY TIME THEY SERVE A SANDWICH!

WELL, WAS IT PEACEFUL TO GET BACK INTO THE WORLD CRISIS AFTER BEING ON LOCATION WITH SAVANNAH GAY AND THE 'SCARLET PRINCESS' COMPANY?

OH, SURE...

BUT WHAT'S THIS FLIMFLAM ABOUT CONDUCTING A SEARCH FOR THE GUY WHO STEPPED IN FOR HUNTLEY SHEFFIELD — THAT'S ME!

THEY'RE STILL 'HUNTING' FOR THE ACTOR PLAYING A UNION SENTRY WHO SIGHED AS LILLIAN GISH WALKED BY IN "BIRTH OF A NATION" IN 1913! IT WAS PROBABLY D.W. GRIFFITH HIMSELF ALL THE TIME!

MILTON CANIFF

AGNES, SLOANE IS BRINGING AROUND A MAN NAMED CANYON WHOM I MAY REPRESENT! I WISH YOU'D TELL ME HOW YOU SIZE HIM UP!

I HATE ACTORS!

THIS FELLOW ISN'T AN ACTOR!

I HATE PEOPLE WHO WANT TO BE ACTORS!

HE DOESN'T WANT TO BE AN ACTOR, AS FAR AS WE KNOW!

... I HATE PEOPLE WHO CAN'T MAKE UP THEIR MINDS!

WELL, THANKS FOR THE CO-OPERATION, DEAR!

ABOVE ALL, I HATE PEOPLE WHO GO AROUND CO-OPERATING!

MILTON CANIFF

STEVE CANYON

MILTON CANIFF

GLAD YOU COULD GET OUT HERE, STEVE! — I MAKE SNIDE REMARKS ABOUT PICTURES...

...BUT I'M REALLY PROUD OF THIS INDUSTRY AND THE GREAT THINGS IT HAS DONE! — NOW, END OF SWEETNESS AND LIGHT AND DOWN TO MONKEY BUSINESS!

QUITE A CHANGE FROM BIG THUNDER, SLOANE... BUT THE MAKE-BELIEVE IS DISCONCERTING...

THERE'S NOTHING MAKE-BELIEVE ABOUT THE DEAL MY AGENT HAS COOKED UP FOR YOU! — THIS IS HIS HOVEL!

COL. CANYON, ONLY FOUR OR FIVE HUNDRED PEOPLE IN HOLLYWOOD KNOW WHO STEPPED IN FOR HUNT SHEFFIELD ON 'SCARLET PRINCESS,' BUT WE PRETEND THERE'S A BIG SEARCH ON FOR YOU...

...THIS GIVES THE COLUMNISTS SOMETHING TO YAK ABOUT — AND DOES THE INDUSTRY NO HARM WITH THE CUSTOMERS...

IF YOU CARE TO LET ME REPRESENT YOU, I WILL GUARANTEE YOU AN ANNUAL INCOME AGAINST THE CERTAINTY THAT YOU WILL EARN MUCH MORE—FOR BOTH OF US...

WHO ARE WE KIDDING? I CAN'T ACT!

THERE ARE SOME FINE ACTORS IN PICTURES, COLONEL, BUT THE BIGGEST MONEYMAKERS ARE THE PERSONALITIES—WHO PLAY THEMSELVES, MORE OR LESS IN EACH FILM...

...FROM YOUR WORK IN 'SCARLET PRINCESS' I'M WILLING TO GAMBLE THAT YOU WILL BE BOX OFFICE!

I DON'T MEAN TO BAD-MOUTH THE AIR FORCE, BUT IT CAN'T OFFER ANYTHING LIKE THIS!

LOOK — I KNOW HOW TO FLY AIRPLANES, BUT AS AN ACTOR—WELL, I WAS GREAT IN MY HIGH SCHOOL SENIOR PLAY!

CANYON, I KNOW HAMS IN THE SIX FIGURE INCOME BELT WHO WEREN'T GREAT IN HIGH SCHOOL—AND ARE GETTING WORSE!

...STEVE, IF YOU'RE NOT SWAYED BY THE PROSPECT OF DIRTY OLD MONEY— I HAVE THE REAL CLINCHER...

FOUR TICKETS TO THE ROSE BOWL GAME!

20

YOU HAVE BOTH BEEN VERY GENEROUS WITH YOUR TIME, GENTLEMEN

I'LL GIVE THIS CAREFUL THOUGHT AND HAVE AN ANSWER AS QUICKLY AS POSSIBLE

ANYTHING SPECIAL YOU'D LIKE TO DO WHILE YOU'RE HERE, STEVE?..ANYONE YOU'D LIKE TO MEET?

I MADE NO PLANS BEYOND WHAT WE'VE BEEN TALKING ABOUT!

MILTON CANIFF

SOME FRIENDS OF MINE ARE HAVING A LITTLE BARN-RAISING AND COMMUNITY-SINGING PARTY OUT IN THE VALLEY... CARE TO INDULGE?

OKAY

HELLO, HERMAN...SLOANE AND COLONEL CANYON JUST LEFT HERE! YOU ALL KNOW WHAT TO DO?

SURE! SURE! —IT'S IN THE BAG!

NOW, THIS IS THE PITCH... SLOANE IS BRINGING THIS AIR FORCE COL. CANYON OUT HERE!

SLOANE AND HIS AGENT THINK CANYON COULD BE BIG IN PICTURES, BUT THE COLONEL WON'T BUY IT...

YOU'VE ALL SEEN THE FILM IN WHICH CANYON DOUBLED FOR HUNT SHEFFIELD... SO THE PLOT IS TO BUTTER UP THE BOY SO HE'LL SIGN

SLOANE'S AGENT SAYS HE IS PLENTY AWARE, SO DON'T BE SCHMALTZY— JUST GIVE HIM THE OLD SOFT SELL...

MILTON CANIFF

HERMAN, I DON'T WANT TO SEEM GRABBY OR COMMERCIAL —BUT WHAT'S IN IT FOR US IF WE SNAG THIS CANYON FOR SLOANE AND THE FLESH PEDDLER?

NOT A THING, SWEETIE, BUT SLOANE IS CASTING NEXT WEEK FOR AN INDEPENDENT—AND THERE ARE SOME JUICY PARTS IN IT FOR TALL REDHEADS!

SAY NO MORE!

21

STEVE CANYON

MILTON CANIFF

STEVE CANYON, DO YOU MEAN TO SAY YOU'RE HAVING TROUBLE DECIDING WHETHER TO STAY IN THE AIR FORCE OR TAKE A FAT SALARY AS AN ACTOR?

THAT'S IT, ALLEE! I HAVE NO ONE LIKE YOU TO ASK FOR ADVICE, BUT AS AN AIR FORCE WIFE YOU PROBABLY HAVE AN OPINION ON THE SUBJECT

YES, IT IS DIFFERENT, FOR A WIFE! MY INITIAL SHOCK WAS BEING UNABLE TO CASH A CHECK AT OUR FIRST STATION... BUT WHAT'S OLD MONEY? – WE HAD FREE MEDICAL CARE AND OUR FIRST CHILD WAS BORN IN A 45-BED WARD THAT WAS ONLY TWO-THIRDS FILLED...

...THE CHILDREN'S BRACES ARE JUST IN PLACE WHEN YOU MOVE...WHICH MEANS A NEW DENTIST! NEW SCHOOLS, NEW FRIENDS AND A NEW CHURCH...THE OLD CURTAINS, AND SUCH, DON'T FIT THE NEW QUARTERS, SO YOU BUY REPLACEMENTS INSTEAD OF THAT NEW DRESS...

...YOU TRY TO FORGET...THE WEDDING GIFTS BROKEN IN THE TURMOIL OF TRANSFERS... THE KIDS CHANGE SCHOOLS SO OFTEN THEY ARE AHEAD OF THE CLASS IN ONE PLACE AND BEHIND IN ANOTHER... AND THE FOUR SNOW SUITS BOUGHT ON SALE IN NEW YORK ARE NO BARGAINS IN THE TRUNK IN PANAMA!

23

...A CROSS-COUNTRY MOVE WITH PAY IS FINE — EXCEPT WHEN, LIKE OURS, THE KIDS COME DOWN WITH MEASLES AND YOU PARK IN A MOTEL FOR DAYS AND GO #300 OVER YOUR ALLOWANCES! ...BUT THEN I LOOK GREAT IN A CLOTH COAT!

AFTER THE THIRD SCOUT MEETING DAD MISSES BECAUSE HE'S ON A FLIGHT, JUNIOR BECOMES A LITTLE IMPATIENT... IF MY HUSBAND IS SENT TO A BASE WHERE DEPENDENTS ARE NOT ALLOWED — THEN THE CAMPING OUT REALLY STARTS...

I HAVEN'T MENTIONED THE SOCIAL REBUFFS WE SOMETIMES GET — OR THE CONSTANT HAUNTING FEAR THAT AT THIS MOMENT YOUR MAN MAY BE LYING DEAD IN A PILE OF SMOKING, TWISTED METAL...

...BUT I'VE BEAT YOUR EAR ENOUGH! — BE SEEING YOU

OH, STEVE, I FORGOT ONE THING...

I WOULDN'T CHANGE PLACES WITH ANY WOMAN IN THE WORLD!

ht 1956, Field Enterprises, Inc

12-23

24

12/24

STEVE, I HAD SOME CUTE STARLETS ALL LINED UP TO GIVE YOU A SELLING JOB ON BECOMING AN ACTOR — BUT YOU ELUDED THEM!

...LET'S PUT IT ON A STRAIGHT MONEY BASIS = MY AGENT CAN GET YOU ENOUGH WORK TO PAY MORE PER MONTH THAN YOU MAKE PER YEAR IN THE AIR FORCE!

I'M TRYING TO HAND YOU A CHRISTMAS GIFT, AND YOU WON'T TAKE IT! YOU GOT SOMETHING AGAINST MAKING MONEY?

FAR FROM IT! BUT I CAN'T AGREE WITH YOU THAT I WOULD MAKE AN ACTOR PEOPLE WOULD PAY TO SEE ON THE SCREEN!

MILTON CANIFF

THIS IS A LAUGH... OUR TOWN IS FULL OF GUYS TRYIN' TO BREAK INTO PICTURES — AND YOU'RE TRYING TO AVOID BEING PULLED INSIDE ...

...MAYBE THAT IS MY CHRISTMAS PRESENT TO THE MOTION PICTURE INDUSTRY, IN RETURN FOR THE FUN IT HAS PROVIDED ME IN THE PAST!

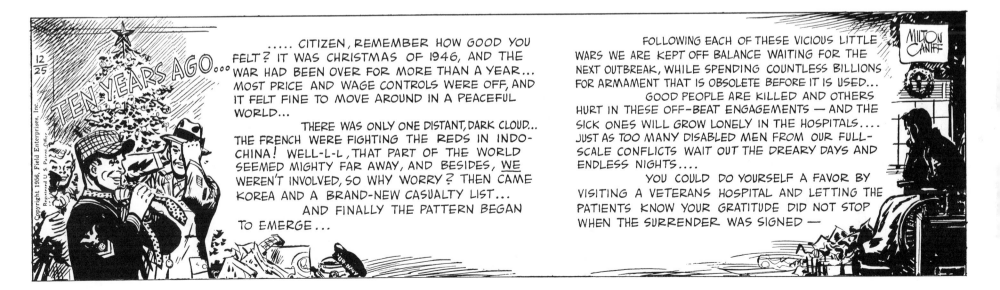

12/25

TEN YEARS AGO...

MILTON CANIFF

..... CITIZEN, REMEMBER HOW GOOD YOU FELT? IT WAS CHRISTMAS OF 1946, AND THE WAR HAD BEEN OVER FOR MORE THAN A YEAR... MOST PRICE AND WAGE CONTROLS WERE OFF, AND IT FELT FINE TO MOVE AROUND IN A PEACEFUL WORLD...

THERE WAS ONLY ONE DISTANT, DARK CLOUD... THE FRENCH WERE FIGHTING THE REDS IN INDO-CHINA! WELL-L-L, THAT PART OF THE WORLD SEEMED MIGHTY FAR AWAY, AND BESIDES, WE WEREN'T INVOLVED, SO WHY WORRY? THEN CAME KOREA AND A BRAND-NEW CASUALTY LIST... AND FINALLY THE PATTERN BEGAN TO EMERGE...

FOLLOWING EACH OF THESE VICIOUS LITTLE WARS WE ARE KEPT OFF BALANCE WAITING FOR THE NEXT OUTBREAK, WHILE SPENDING COUNTLESS BILLIONS FOR ARMAMENT THAT IS OBSOLETE BEFORE IT IS USED...

GOOD PEOPLE ARE KILLED AND OTHERS HURT IN THESE OFF-BEAT ENGAGEMENTS — AND THE SICK ONES WILL GROW LONELY IN THE HOSPITALS.... JUST AS TOO MANY DISABLED MEN FROM OUR FULL-SCALE CONFLICTS WAIT OUT THE DREARY DAYS AND ENDLESS NIGHTS....

YOU COULD DO YOURSELF A FAVOR BY VISITING A VETERANS HOSPITAL AND LETTING THE PATIENTS KNOW YOUR GRATITUDE DID NOT STOP WHEN THE SURRENDER WAS SIGNED —

SERGEANT, THIS MAN IS CARRYING AN IDENTITY CARD WHICH SAYS HE IS LT. COL. STEVENSON B. CANYON, USAFR!

BUT IF HE'S AN AIR FORCE OFFICER, WHAT'S HE DOING TAKIN' A WALK?

BUT IF YOU ARE AN AIR FORCE OFFICER, WHAT WERE YOU DOING WANDERING AROUND THE AREA AT NIGHT?

TRYING TO DECIDE WHETHER TO TAKE A FAT CIVILIAN JOB —OR STAY ON ACTIVE DUTY!

I GUESS WE'VE ALL BEEN THROUGH THAT WRINGER BEFORE! —YOUR PAPERS ARE IN ORDER, SIR! WHAT ARE YOU GOING TO DO NOW?

I THINK I'LL BUM A RIDE ON AN AIRPLANE... MAYBE THE TRIP WILL CLEAR MY HEAD!

COL. CANYON, WE HAVE A BIRD GOING INTO WRIGHT-PATTERSON ON A TURNAROUND! WANT TO RIDE ALONG?

OKAY

HELLO, SLOANE! I'M CADGING AN AIRPLANE RIDE! WE'LL REFUEL AT DAYTON! I'LL CALL YOU FROM THERE

WHILE STEVE CANYON PONDERS HIS FUTURE, POTEET CANYON HAS ANOTHER KIND OF PROBLEM...

IS IT TIME?

YEAH

GET READY! HERE SHE COMES NOW!

27

STEVE CANYON

by Milton Caniff

WHAT IS STEVE CANYON'S DECISION ABOUT COMING TO HOLLYWOOD?

HE TOOK AN AIR FORCE FLIGHT BACK EAST TO CLEAR HIS HEAD, AS HE PUT IT...

HE'LL CALL US FROM THEIR REFUELING STOP AT WRIGHT-PATTERSON AIR FORCE BASE...

I COME TO THE AIR FORCE CENTRAL MUSEUM OFTEN, BUT I NEVER SAW YOU HERE BEFORE, MISTER...

I'M JUST PASSING THROUGH DAYTON! THIS IS MY FIRST VISIT!

THEN MAYBE I CAN SHOW YOU AROUND WHILE MY MOTHER IS MAKING A PHONE CALL!.. THIS IS THE REPRODUCTION OF THE FIRST AMERICAN MILITARY AIRPLANE!... MY DADDY SAYS I SHOULD NEVER FORGET THAT IT CAME FROM RIGHT HERE WHERE I LIVE...

THIS IS ONE OF THE SPADS OUR PILOTS HAD TO FLY IN THE FIRST WORLD WAR-BECAUSE WE ONLY OWNED 55 AIRCRACT WHEN THE U.S. ENTERED! MY DADDY SAYS I MUST ALWAYS REMEMBER THE MEN WHO BUILT AN AIR FORCE ON COURAGE AND HOPE!

YOU PROBABLY RECOGNIZE THE P-51 FROM WORLD WAR II...

WHY—AH—YES...I DO!

THIS IS OUR FIRST JET TO SET A WORLD'S SPEED RECORD...623.8 mph! AND THE PILOT DID IT ON AIR FORCE PAY!... MY DADDY SAYS WE GET MORE STRAIGHT, RAW BRAVERY PER DOLLAR FOR OUR TAX MONEY THAN ANY OTHER COUNTRY!

MY DADDY SAYS THAT THE SLIDE RULE MEN MAY GET MORE SALARY, BUT THEIR PATRIOTISM IS JUST AS GREAT AS THE AIR CREWS—AS LONG AS THEY KEEP GIVING THE COMBAT MEN SUPERIOR WEAPONS...

OH, DEAR, THERE'S MY MOTHER, LOOKING FOR ME! I'M GLAD YOU CAME OUT TO THE MUSEUM! NOT MANY PEOPLE HERE TO START THE 50th YEAR OF MILITARY AVIATION!

YOU QUOTE YOUR FATHER SO OFTEN — IS HE IN THE AIR FORCE?

HE WAS!...DADDY WAS SHOT DOWN IN KOREA...BUT I RE-READ THE LETTERS HE WROTE WHEN I WAS A BABY! I DIDN'T HAVE A CHANCE TO KNOW HIM, BUT I SHALL ALWAYS LOVE THE THINGS HE LOVED! —'BYE, MISTER!

THIS IS SLOANE SPEAKING!

STEVE CANYON CALLING! I'VE DISCUSSED THINGS WITH COUNSEL — AND DECIDED TO STAY IN THE AIR FORCE!

12-30

29

DARK-HORSE TEAM

JANUARY 1 to
APRIL 12, 1957

33

STEVE CANYON

by MILTON CANIFF

GOOD NEWS! WE'VE WORKED OUT A TUITION PLAN WITH THE BIG THUNDER SCHOOLS... YOU KIDS WON'T HAVE TO TRAVEL 20 MILES A DAY TO THE CONSOLIDATED SCHOOL ACROSS THE MOUNTAIN!

OH...?

THE BIG THUNDER SCHOOLS WILL SEND TEACHERS HERE TO TUTOR THE VERY YOUNG ONES!... ISN'T THAT GREAT?

WHY, YES, SIR, COUSIN STEVIE B.

COUSIN STEVIE, WOULD YOU AN' THE OTHER KINDLY FOLKS THINK HARSH OF ME IF I KEPT ON AT STUMPHILL CONSOLIDATED SCHOOL?

I—I KNOW THEY SHOULDN'T SEND THE SCHOOL BUS ALL THE WAY HERE FOR ONE STUDENT...

BUT THE MILK TRUCK MAKES A ROUND TRIP EVERY DAY... I KNOW I CAN HITCH A RIDE!

WELL, POTEET, I DON'T BELIEVE IN KIDS CHANGING SCHOOLS IF NOT ABSOLUTELY NECESSARY, SO CONTINUE AT STUMP-HILL, IF YOU LIKE!

OH, THANK YOU, COUSIN STEVIE!

THEN, IF Y'ALL WILL EXCUSE ME, I'LL GO DO MY HOMEWORK!

SHE SEEMED TO HATE SCHOOL AT FIRST! NOW SHE IS THE FIRST ONE OUT IN THE MORNING — AND SHE STAYS LONG AFTER CLASSES!

WHILE YOU WERE ON LEAVE I WAS TOO BUSY GETTING THE BASE IN SHAPE TO PAY MUCH ATTENTION!

POTEET ACTED BROKEN TO HARNESS, BUT I DIDN'T KNOW SHE LIKED STUMP-HILL THAT MUCH!

DOES SHE HAVE A BOY FRIEND OVER THERE?

IF I KNOW POTEET, SHE PROBABLY HAS SIX OF THEM!

... WHICH IS EXACTLY HOW MANY BOYS SHE HAS A DATE WITH...

SHHH-H! HERE COMES THE COACH!

1-6

TORRY, I'M SCHEDULED TO SIT IN ON THE ARMY ANTI-AIRCRAFT POW-WOW AT FORT RUNKLE! BE BACK AS SOON AS I CAN!

ROGER, STEVE!

LATER

HI, KIDS! HOW DID IT GO ON YOUR FIRST DAY BACK IN THE BIG THUNDER SCHOOLS?

NEGATIVE, MAJOR TORR!.. WE MISS HAVING POTEET ON HAND TO STAND UP FOR US IF WE GET KICKED AROUND!

SHE GOT PERMISSION FROM COL. CANYON TO STAY AT STUMPHILL CONSOLIDATED INSTEAD OF TRANSFERRING WITH YOU — SO I GUESS SHE MUST THINK YOU CAN TAKE CARE OF YOURSELVES!

SHALL WE TELL HIM POTEET REALLY STAYED AT STUMPHILL BECAUSE SHE IS COACH, TRAINER, MANAGER, TREASURER AND HOUSEMOTHER OF THE BASKETBALL TEAM?

YES! IF HE KNOWS, IT MEANS WE MAY GET OUR QUARTERS BACK FOR THE STOCK SHE SOLD US TO BUY A BASKETBALL!

MAJOR TORR, WE CAME TO TALK ABOUT POTEET!

COL. CANYON IS AT THE ARMY FORT FOR A FEW DAYS, I--

WE KNOW, SIR! WE'RE HERE TO TALK TO YOU ABOUT HER!

NOW THAT WE HAVE BEEN TRANSFERRED BACK TO THE BIG THUNDER SCHOOLS, SHE WON'T BE COLLECTING OUR LUNCH MONEY TO GET WHOLE-SALE PRICES BY COLLECTIVE BUYING!

IT WAS BETTER FOOD, SIR, BUT SHE SCARED US INTO PAYING!

POTEET DECIDED TO ORGANIZE ATHLETICS AT STUMPHILL SCHOOL! SHE IS THE COACH OF THE BASKETBALL TEAM, BUT THE SCHOOL IS SO POOR SHE HAD TO SELL STOCK TO BUY A BALL!

NOW WE'RE AFRAID WE WON'T EVER BE ALLOWED TO PLAY ON SCHOOL TEAMS BECAUSE WE GAVE MONEY TO AMA-TEUR ATHLETES!

36

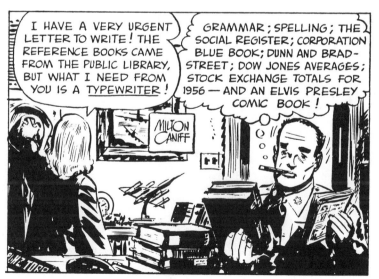

THANK YOU, MAJOR TORR! IT'S MIGHTY KINDLY OF YOU TO LEND ME THE TYPE-WRITER!

MM-M-M— YOU'RE -AH- WELCOME, POTEET!

WELL, TORRY, OUR FRIENDS IN THE ARMY SENT THEIR REGARDS TO ALL US AIR FORCE CHARACTERS!

I'M GLAD YOU GOT BACK ALIVE, STEVE! —ALTHOUGH I DON'T KNOW WHETHER THIS END WILL BE ANY EASIER THAN TALKING GUIDED MISSILES TO THE ARMY!

DID POTEET SHOOT SOMEBODY, OR DID SOMEBODY SHOOT POTEET? EITHER POSSIBILITY WOULD HORRIFY ME, BUT IT WOULDN'T SURPRISE ME!

I WANT YOU TO GET VERY COMFORTABLE BEFORE I TELL YOU..! —WE DON'T WANT TO LOSE GOOD MEN LIKE YOU FROM THE SERVICE DUE TO BURST CYLINDER HEADS!!

MILTON CANIFF

STEVE, I DON'T KNOW EXACTLY HOW TO TELL YOU, BUT POTEET IS THE COACH OF STUMP-HILL SCHOOL'S BASKET-BALL TEAM!

POOR OLD TORRY! YOU SHOULD HAVE TAKEN THAT LEAVE IN HOLLYWOOD! THE PRESSURE OF OPENING BIG THUNDER BASE HAS BENT YOUR RUDDER!

NO SNOW, STEVE — AND I WAS NEVER MORE RATIONAL!.. POTEET HASN'T PEEPED, BUT THE KIDS FILLED ME IN FOR THEIR OWN PROTECTION!

SHE HAS ONLY SIX BOYS ON HER SQUAD — SO WHAT SCARED THE OTHER STUDENTS WAS WHEN SHE TRIED TO ORGANIZE AN EXPEDITION TO THE STATE CAPITAL...

...TO PICKET THE STATE BOARD OF EDUCATION TO GET A RULE ALLOWING GIRLS TO PLAY ON BOYS' BASKETBALL TEAMS!

MILTON CANIFF

SHE'S THE COACH AT STUMPHILL SCHOOL?

YES, STEVE... IT HAPPENED WHILE YOU WERE ON LEAVE, BUT THE KIDS WERE SCARED TO TELL US UNTIL THEY TRANSFERRED BACK TO THE BIG THUNDER SCHOOL!

THEY HAVE NO ORGANIZED ATHLETICS AT THE STUMPHILL CONSOLIDATED SCHOOL! POTEET STOOD IT AS LONG AS SHE COULD...

"THEN SHE HEARD OF A BARN THAT WAS FILLED WITH A SURPLUS CROP THAT HAD SPOILED. SHE MADE A DEAL WITH THE FARMER FOR THE HIGH SCHOOL KIDS TO CLEAR THE BUILDING IN RETURN FOR USING IT AS A BASKETBALL COURT...

"... ONLY SIX BOYS TURNED OUT FOR PRACTICE... AND, SINCE THEY HAD NO COACH, IT WAS PRETTY PATHETIC...

"...FINALLY POTEET UPS AND ANNOUNCED THAT SHE WOULD BE THE COACH! WHEN SOMEONE QUESTIONED IT, SHE ASKED IF THEY HAD HEARD OF THE LATE BABE DIDRIKSON ZAHARIAS WHO WAS ANOTHER TEXAS GIRL AND ONE ANY BOYS' TEAM WOULD HAVE WELCOMED AS A COACH..."

"...SHE WROTE SCHOOLS IN THE AREA OFFERING TO PLAY THEM PRACTICE GAMES BETWEEN THEIR REGULAR SCHEDULED CONTESTS..."

"...FINALLY RIVERTOWN HIGH HAD A CANCELLATION AND POTEET GRABBED AT THE DATE — THEY'RE PRACTICING FOR IT THIS WEEK..."

SHE ASKED TO BORROW AN OFFICE TYPEWRITER TO WRITE AN EXTRA SPECIAL LETTER TO SOMEONE!... FRANKLY, I'M HOLDING MY BREATH!

January 13, 1957

Miss Copper Calhoon
Calhoon Industries,
Chicago, Illinois

Dear Miss Calhoon:
   I have learned that you are the largest stockholder in the Stumphill Mine. I am Coach of the Stumphill Consolidated School Boys' Basketball Team. Will you get us a discount on uniforms through the Company Store?
   Your fellow-Woman Executive,
(Miss) Poteet Canyon

Encl.: List of Measurements.

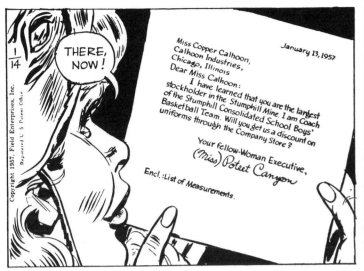

WHAT'S THE JOKE?

JUST AN UNUSUAL LETTER IN MISS CALHOON'S MAIL, MRS. OLSON...

"DEAR MISS CALHOON =
I HAVE LEARNED THAT YOU ARE THE LARGEST STOCKHOLDER IN THE STUMPHILL MINE. I AM COACH OF THE STUMPHILL CONSOLIDATED SCHOOL BOYS' BASKETBALL TEAM. WILL YOU GET US A DISCOUNT ON UNIFORMS THROUGH THE COMPANY STORE?

YOUR FELLOW-WOMAN EXECUTIVE (MISS) POTEET CANYON"

HEY! YOU CAN'T GO IN THERE!

BUT, MISTER, WE'RE THE VISITIN' TEAM FROM STUMPHILL SCHOOL! HERE'S OUR INVITATION!

WELL—ALL RIGHT! BUT YOU CAN'T GO INTO THE LOCKER ROOM, MISS!

BUT I'M THE COACH!

THEN YOU'LL HAVE TO INSPIRE THEM BY TELEPHONE!

AND WHILE THIS IS HAPPENING AN AIR EXPRESS PACKAGE ARRIVES AT RIVERTOWN

WELL, NOW— A SPECIAL-HANDLING PACKAGE FOR THE VISITIN' BASKETBALL TEAM! THIS IS ONE TIME I SEE A GAME FOR FREE!

43

STEVE CANYON

by MILTON CANIFF

MRS. OLSON, HERE IS MISS CALHOON'S PERSONAL MAIL COUNT FOR THE DAY...20 INVITATIONS, 162 REQUESTS FOR CONTRIBUTIONS AND FOUR THREATS OF VIOLENCE!

THERE'S ONE BEGGING LETTER THAT IS SORT OF CUTE...

MRS. OLSON YOU'RE PALE! ARE YOU ILL?

N-NO...IT'S JUST THIS SIGNATURE—"POTEET CANYON"—IT'S UNUSUAL! I USED TO KNOW SOMEONE WITH THAT SAME LAST NAME!

OLSON!! ANYTHING AMUSING IN THE LUNATIC MAIL THIS MORNING?

NO, MISS CALHOON —NOT A THING!

LATER...

WHAT'S THIS STUMPHILL HIGH? I THOUGHT RIVERTOWN WAS PLAYING NEW RUSHVILLE!

THERE WAS A POLIO THREAT AT NEW RUSHVILLE, SO THEY CANCELLED THE SEASON! STUMPHILL IS A MINING CENTER WEST OF HERE...OWNED BY THE COPPER CALHOON INTERESTS!

RIVERTOWN STUMPHILL

LOOK AT THAT BUNCH OF YOKELS—AND THEIR COACH IS A *GIRL*!

THIS IS A BASKETBALL TEAM?

THEY DON'T EVEN HAVE UNIFORMS!

DID YOU HEAR WHAT THEY CALLED US? 'SCARECROWS'!

I FEEL KINDA FOOLISH! THEY YELLED 'RAGPICKER' AT ME!

THAT'S WHAT THE BRITISH SAID ABOUT THE CONTINENTAL ARMY!

BUT, MISS POTEET, WE'RE NOT IN ANY ARMY!—WE'RE JUS' BOYS FROM STUMPHILL!

HEY, MISS! YOU MAY BE THE COACH OF THIS—AH—TEAM, BUT YOU CAN'T GO INTO THE BOYS' LOCKER ROOM!

OH—I JUS' DOWNRIGHT FORGOT!

I GOT A SPECIAL-HANDLING PACKAGE FOR MISS POTEET CANYON, CARE OF THE VISITIN' TEAM!

THE PACKAGE CONTAINS A COMPLETE SET OF BASKETBALL UNIFORMS FROM SUMMER OLSON... BUT *WHAT* UNIFORMS! POTEET REALIZES THAT THIS IS THE MARGIN OF HIGH OR LOW MORALE—SO SHE MAKES AN ARRANGEMENT WITH THE ATTENDANT... AND WHEN HER SQUAD IS ALL SUITED UP TO GO OUT FOR THE GAME...

...THE FRIENDLY JANITOR PULLS THE SWITCH AND THE STUMPHILL TEAM RUNS ON IN *FLUORESCENT* COLORS!!!

—20

1/21

TO THE SURPRISE OF THE RIVERTOWN HIGH SCHOOL FANS, THE RAGTAG STUMP-HILL BASKETBALL TEAM COMES ON AFTER WARMUP PRACTICE WEARING FLUORESCENT UNIFORMS OF BRIGHT YELLOW AND RED

FOR PETE'S SAKE, COACH, WHAT **IS** THIS?—SOME KINDA PSYCHO-LOGICAL WARFARE?

I DON'T KNOW, BUT THEY STILL HANDLE THE BALL AS IF IT WERE A PUMPKIN!

WOW, POTEET! WE REALLY ROCKED 'EM WITH OUR NEW UNIFORMS!

WE'VE GOT 'EM PUZZLED 'CAUSE WE HAVE NO PLAYIN' RECORD! DON'T GET BIGGITY! —JUS' DO LIKE WE PRACTICED—AND HOPE!

WHILE IN CHICAGO...

I'M SORRY MRS. OLSON WE HAVE NO REPORT ON HIGH SCHOOL GAMES FROM THAT AREA...

BUT OF COURSE THAT MAY BE IN ANOTHER TIME ZONE —OR SOMETHING!

1/22

THE GAME BEGINS: STUMPHILL'S TALL CENTER GETS THE TIP — AND SLAPS THE BALL HARD TO THE SIDELINES

THE STUMPHILL GUARD TAKES THE PASS AND IN ONE MOTION FIRES IT AT THE DISTANT BACKBOARD

THE GREAT HEAVE BOUNCES FAR, BUT THE STUMPHILL FORWARD IS WAITING AT THE PRECISE SPOT...

AND DRIBBLES IN FOR AN EASY LAYUP SHOT — AND STUMPHILL IS AHEAD 2-0!

46

THE UNSEASONED STUMPHILL PLAYERS ARE SO ELATED BY THEIR QUICK SCORE THAT THEY DO NOT GET SET FOR THE RIVERTOWN ATTACK

RIVERTOWN SCORES WITH EASE —AND AS STUMPHILL PUTS THE BALL BACK INTO PLAY THE GUARD AGAIN FIRES IT ALL THE WAY DOWN THE COURT TO THE BACKBOARD...

THIS TIME THE STUMP-HILL MAN WAITING FOR THE LONG REBOUND STARTS TO DRIBBLE IN FOR HIS LAYUP —AND FINDS A SOLID WALL OF OPPONENTS...

I WOULDN'T HAVE BELIEVED IT, BUT THESE KIDS HAVE ONLY ONE PLAY! FENNER, GO IN AND BIRD-DOG THAT TALL CENTER!

HE'S THE ONLY FRONT-COURT MAN THEY HAVE WHO CAN HIT THE BASKET!

RIVERTOWN SOLVES POTEET'S ONE STRATE-GEM IN THE FIRST FEW MINUTES OF PLAY —AND THE PANIC IS ON

EVEN THOUGH STUMPHILL GETS THE BALL AFTER EACH RIVERTOWN SCORE, ITS INEXPERIENCED PLAYERS ARE UNABLE TO BREAK THROUGH THE OTHER TEAM'S DEFENSE...

BY THE END OF THE GAME THE ROUT HAS BECOME LUDICROUS... AND AT THE FINAL GUN EVEN THE RIVERTOWN STUDENTS ARE TOO EMBARRASSED TO JEER...

... POTEET MARCHES RESO-LUTELY ACROSS THE FLOOR TO CONGRATULATE THE RIVAL COACH — THEN JUST MAKES IT OUT OF THE GYM BEFORE SHE BURSTS INTO TEARS...

1-27

50

GEE, POTEET, DON'T LOOK SO SAD! WE'VE GOT THESE SWELL UNIFORMS

...AN' THE PRINCIPAL OF STUMPHILL SCHOOL CONGRATULATED US FOR GETTIN' UP A TEAM!

EVEN THE FELLAHS WHO HANG OUT AT THE SMOKE SHOP DIDN'T RAZZ US WHEN WE WALKED PAST...

OH, WE'RE A RIGHT BIG SOCIAL SUCCESS...

BUT WE STILL CAN'T PLAY BASKETBALL WORTH TWO CENTS!

"DEAR MRS. OLSON — IT WAS DOWNRIGHT NEIGHBORLY OF YOU TO SEND US THE ELEGANT BASKETBALL SUITS...

"THEY WERE THE HIT OF THE GAME WITH RIVERTOWN... WE ONLY LOST, 78 TO 22...

"WE CAN'T GET ANY MORE GAMES UNTIL THE STATE TOURNAMENT, BUT WE WILL PAY FOR THE UNIFORMS OUT OF OUR LUNCH MONEY...

"ALL WE COULD COLLECT FOR THE FIRST PAYMENT IS ONE DOLLAR. A MONEY ORDER IS ENCLOSED...

GRATEFULLY,

(MISS) POTEET CANYON (COACH)"

OLSON! WHY ARE YOU SITTING OUT HERE BLUBBERING?

WOW, STEVE, WHAT'S THIS? HAS THAT AIR POLICEMAN PINCHED ALL THOSE MEN?

IF HE DID, WHY IS HE BRINGING THEM HERE?

SIR, WE HAVE CAPT. PICKREL'S PERMISSION TO SPEAK TO THE COLONEL!

OKAY— —GO AHEAD!

BEGGIN' THE COLONEL'S WARD'S PARDON, SIR... SOME OF US SAW MISS POTEET CANYON'S TEAM PLAY BASKETBALL OVER AT RIVERTOWN LAST WEEK! SIR, THOSE KIDS REALLY SMELLED UP THE GYM!

WELL?

SIR, ALL OF US PLAYED HIGH SCHOOL BASKETBALL!.. ON OUR OFF TIME WE'D LIKE TO WORK OUT WITH THOSE STUMPHILL KIDS! WOULD SHE THINK WE WERE OUT OF ORDER— OR JUST NUTS?

WELL, I DO DECLARE! THAT MRS. OLSON IN MISS COPPER CALHOON'S OFFICE WON'T TAKE MONEY FOR OUR UNIFORMS!

YOU MEAN THEY'RE OURS — FOR FREE?

YES, BUT SHE AN' MISS CALHOON ARE COMIN' FOR THE STATE TOURNAMENT! SHE'LL SEE US PLAY IN THEM!

THAT'S AWFUL!

WE'VE GOT TO IMPROVE! WE'LL FIND A SQUAD TO PRACTICE AGAINST—

—EVEN IF I HAVE TO OR- GANIZE A GIRLS' TEAM FOR YOU TO SCRIMMAGE WITH!

WHEN ?

WHERE ?

WHO ?

WHICH ?

WHEE!

53

AND SO THE AIR FORCE VOLUNTEERS BEGIN A MAN-TO-MAN COACHING JOB AS THEY TEACH THE STUMPHILL KIDS HOW TO PLAY EACH POSITION...

FORGET THE FANCY DAN STUFF! JUST GET THE BALL IN THE BASKET!

BE AGGRESSIVE, BUT DON'T FOUL! YOU CAN'T SCORE FROM THE BENCH!

GET THERE FIRST—BUT BRING THE BALL WITH YOU!

THEY'RE STARTING TO MOVE, COUSIN STEVIE B.! MRS. OLSON WILL BE RIGHT PROUD!

MRS. WHO WILL BE WHAT?

WHY, MRS. OLSON OF THE COPPER CALHOON COMPANY—WHICH 'OWNS' THE TOWN OF STUMPHILL! I WROTE FOR HELP TO BUY OUR UNIFORMS—AND THIS KINDLY MRS. O. JUST SENT THEM TO US AND WOULDN'T TAKE A PENNY!

IT'S OUR SECRET... AN' WHEN MISS CALHOON AN' MRS. OLSON ARE VISITIN' HERE DURING THE STATE TOURNAMENT, I'M NOT TO BREATHE WHERE THE SUITS CAME FROM!

YOU LOOK KINDA FROWNY, COUSIN! —DID I DO SOMETHING WRONG ALONG THE LINE?

NO, POTEET —I DID!

2-3

55

OH, COUSIN STEVIE B., _THIS_ IS THE WAY TO DO IT...

MY STUMPHILL KIDS ARE REALLY LEARNING TO PLAY THE GAME BY WORKIN' OUT WITH THE BIG THUNDER AIRMEN!

...BUT YOU'RE ACTIN' REAL THOUGHTY! WHAT DID I SAY OUT OF LINE?

NOTHING, POTEET! I WAS STARTLED TO LEARN THAT SUMMER OLSON HAD SENT YOU THE BASKETBALL UNIFORMS!

SHE DIDN'T TELL _ME_ HER FIRST NAME — SO I RECKON YOU KNOW THAT KINDLY LADY!

—I ONCE KNEW HER VERY WELL! HER HUSBAND IS STILL AN INVALID FROM A MISSION I SENT HIM ON!

THEN...SHE...ISN'T A...WIDOW — SO I DON'T HAVE TO WORRY BECAUSE SHE'S COMING HERE WITH MISS CALHOON!

WHAT ARE YOU MUMBLING ABOUT?

AH—JUS' FIGURIN' OUT SOME FUTURE STRATEGY!

OLSON! WHAT'S THIS WAD OF PAPER MARKED "STUMPHILL MINE REPORT"?

IT'S THE USUAL CRITIQUE ON ONE OF YOUR PROPERTIES THAT IS NOT PRODUCING TO CAPACITY, MISS CALHOON!

BUT YOU ALWAYS GIVE ME A RESUMÉ! I CAN'T WADE THROUGH ALL THAT GUFF!...

IT NEEDS TOP-LEVEL THINKING, MA'AM! THESE ARE EXPERTS' REPORTS THAT EVERY STANDARD DEVICE HAS BEEN USED TO STEP UP CARLOADINGS...

...YET PRODUCTION STILL DROPS. I MADE INQUIRIES AND CAME ON A POSSIBLE SOLUTION. MY REPORT IS IN THERE, TOO...

GIVE IT TO ME VERBALLY IN TWO MINUTES...AND IT HAD BETTER BE GOOD, OR I'LL WALK OUT ON YOU!

2-10

LADIES, THE LIEUTENANT TELLS ME YOUR AIRCRAFT LANDED HERE UNDER EMERGENCY CONDITIONS

I HOPE YOU WILL ACCEPT A STAFF CAR AND DRIVER TO TRANSPORT YOU ANYWHERE YOU WISH TO GO...

THERE IS A VERY DECENT RESTAURANT DOWN THE ROAD THAT HAS BETTER FOOD THAN WE CAN OFFER YOU HERE AT THIS TIME OF DAY!

THIS IS MORE LIKE IT! WE ACCEPT!

I DID IT JUST AS YOU SAID TO, STEVE! REMEMBER, YOU PROMISED TO TELL ME WHAT THIS IS ALL ABOUT!

IT'S SOMETHING TO HELP POTEET'S BASKETBALL TEAM...BUT IF THE COPPER-HAIRED WOMAN HAD SEEN ME SHE'D PROBABLY HAVE PERSONALLY FLOWN HER AIRCRAFT OUT OF HERE WITHOUT BOTHERING TO START THE ENGINES!

TORRY, POTEET HOPED THAT COPPER CALHOON'S VISIT TO STUMPHILL WOULD RAISE THE MORALE OF THE MINING TOWN SO THEY'LL RALLY 'ROUND THE BASKETBALL TEAM...

SHE ALSO HOPES THAT COPPER WILL PHONE THE STATE ATHLETIC BOARD AND MAKE CERTAIN STUMPHILL IS ACCEPTED IN THE STATE TOURNAMENT, IN SPITE OF HAVING PLAYED NO REGULAR SCHEDULE

I WAS ONCE ENGAGED TO MARRY THE SECRETARY, SUMMER OLSON, AND IF COPPER KNEW I WAS HERE SHE'D BE OFF AND RUNNING — AND POTEET'S BIG SHOW WOULD BE SHOT!

MEANWHILE

DRIVER, WE'LL GO RIGHT TO THE HOTEL!

BUT, MA'AM, THERE'S NO HOTEL IN STUMPHILL!

ALL RIGHT, OLSON, START TALKING... AND WHATEVER YOUR EXCUSE, IT HAD BETTER BE THE BEST ONE YOUR SENTIMENTAL LITTLE SKULL EVER HATCHED!

62

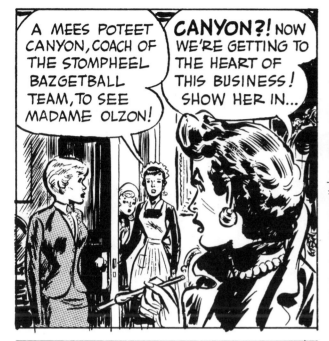

2-17

65

DOES THAT WOMAN HAVE SOME HOLD ON YOU THAT YOU SHOULD TAKE SUCH ABUSE FROM HER?

IT'S ONLY A JOB! WHERE YOU WORK YOUR BOSS CAN ORDER YOU TO GO OUT AND GIVE YOUR LIFE—AND YOU'VE TAKEN AN OATH TO OBEY!

OH, SUMMER! WHY DO WE ALWAYS FIGHT? IT MAY BE WRONG, BUT I LOVE YOU—AND THAT'S THAT!

—AND THAT'S AS FAR AS IT CAN GO, STEVE! YOU'D BETTER LEAVE —NOW!

YOU REENG, MEES CALHOON?

AFTER MRS. OLSON HAS HAD HER CRY, BRING ME THE MIDGET TAPE RECORDER YOU PLANTED IN THE ROOM! —I'M LOOKING FORWARD TO A LITTLE QUIET PRIVATE SOAP OPERA!

2-24

RIGHT WHEN I'VE GOT MY SCHOOLWORK AND THE FIRST ROUND OF THE STATE BASKETBALL TOURNAMENT ON MY MIND...

...YOU COME ALONG WITH THIS HEADACHE FOR ME!

WHAT ARE YOU GOING TO DO ABOUT IT, LITTLE ORPHAN WHOZIS?

MA'AM, I DON'T TAKE KINDLY TO FOLKS WHO ARE ORN'RY JUS' FOR JOLLIES!

I'M FRIGHTENED OUT OF MY WITS!.. AND I AM ALSO BECOMING BORED!

NOW GO AWAY BEFORE I CALL THE POLICE!

MEANWHILE...THE PAIRINGS HAVE BEEN DRAWN FOR THE REGIONAL TOURNAMENTS...

IN THE B DIVISION... WEST OLEANDREA PLAYS STUMPHILL!

I'LL BET THE WIRE SERVICES WILL GIVE THAT ONE A BIG PLAY!

STEVE, I DON'T MEAN TO DISTRESS YOU, BUT COPPER CALHOON ORDERED ME TO GO TO THESE GAMES...

BECAUSE SHE KNEW I'D BE HERE ON ACCOUNT OF POTEET! I'M GLAD TO SEE YOU, SUMMER, HONEY! EVEN THOUGH IT HURTS — IT HURTS GOOD!

REGION 4 STATE BASKET

Copyright 1957, Field Enterprises, Inc.

3-3

75

SUMMER, I THINK THE COPPERHEAD OUT-FOXED HERSELF BY ORDERING YOU TO ATTEND THIS TOURNAMENT!

YOU ARE NOT FREE TO MARRY ME, BUT I AM GLAD TO SEE YOU ENJOYING YOURSELF FOR ONCE!

IT IS FUN, STEVE!.... SEEING A BASKETBALL GAME TAKES ME BACK TO WHEN LOTS OF THINGS WERE DIFFERENT!

I DON'T THINK I EVER TOLD YOU I WAS A CHEER-LEADER, DID I?

AND ALL THE TIME I THOUGHT YOU WERE THE MAJORETTE TYPE!

OH! HERE COME POTEET AND HER STUMPHILL TEAM! DO THEY HAVE ANY CHANCE AT ALL, STEVE?

IF THEY DON'T WIN THIS FIRST GAME THERE WON'T BE A LOOSE DOLLAR BILL AT BIG THUNDER AIR FORCE BASE UNTIL NEXT PAYDAY!

THE WEST OLEANDREA PIVOT MAN SEEMS TO BE LEFT-HANDED! PRESS HIM ON HIS WEAK SIDE AND DON'T LET UP!

GEE, POTEET, DO YOU REALLY THINK WE CAN WIN? WE'VE NEVER ACTUALLY BEEN IN A---

NOW HUSH UP THAT TALK! MEN HAVE WON THE CONGRESSIONAL MEDAL OF HONOR THEIR FIRST TIME IN COMBAT!

WE'RE GONNA DO JUS' LIKE THE AIRMEN TOLD US!—AN' WE'RE GONNA BE POISED! POISED! **POISED!**

BUT STUMPHILL IS JUST A DIRTY LITTLE MINING TOWN! NOTHIN' MUCH GOOD EVER CAME FROM THERE...

STUMPHILL IS THE CAPITAL OF CREATION! EVERY TIME YOU HIT THAT BASKET YOUR DADS ARE GONNA BE CLOSER TO THE TOP OF THE WORLD—EVEN THOUGH THEY'RE AT THE BOTTOM OF THE MINE SHAFT!

...AND I RECKON THE STUMPHILL PLAYER I'M GONNA GO STEADY WITH AFTER THE TOURNAMENT KNOWS WHICH ONE HE IS!...

FIRST PERIOD

SAY! WHICH GAME IS THIS? THOSE KIDS ARE SMOOTH!

STUMPHILL SCHOOL VS. WEST OLEANDREA.. DIVISION B ELIMINATIONS

SECOND PERIOD

STEVE, IS THIS THE SAME STUMPHILL TEAM THAT LOST ITS ONLY OTHER GAME, 78 to 22 ?

I THINK SO, SUMMER, BUT IT MIGHT BE A TYPO- GRAPHICAL ERROR IN THE PROGRAM

THIRD PERIOD

COME ON, WEST OLEY! WE HAD SUCH A GOOD YEAR! DON'T GO DOWN IN THE FIRST GAME!

AND WE THOUGHT STUMPHILL WAS SOME SORT OF A JOKE!

FOURTH PERIOD

STEVE! THEY MADE IT!

BUT I COLLECT THE REWARD!

MILTON CANIFF

STEVE, POTEET'S BOYS WON THEIR FIRST GAME!... WHAT HAPPENS NOW?

TONIGHT THEY PLAY THE WINNER OF THE MILL CITY-OBERDEEN GAME!

MAY WE GO TO THEIR DORM AND CONGRATULATE POTEET WITHOUT JINXING THE TEAM?

THEY'RE PROBABLY TOO KEYED UP TO KNOW WE'RE NEAR!

I WANT EVERY MAN TO LIE STILL AS A STICK AN' SOAK UP ALL THE ENERGY THE CLOCK WILL ALLOW...

EVEN IF THE PLAYER I INTEND T'GO STEADY WITH IS THE FIRST T'MOVE— I'LL CHANGE MY MIND AN' BE AN OLD MAID!

MILTON CANIFF

WHERE'S OLSON?

MEES CALHOON, YOU SEND HER TO BAZGETBALL MATCH! MAY-BEE EES NOT YET COMPLETE!

I'LL TELEPHONE THE MINE OFFICE! SOME-ONE ON MY PAYROLL MUST KNOW WHAT'S HAPPENING!

STUMPHILL NUMBER TWO

DO YOU KNOW WHAT'S GOING ON AT THAT BASKET-BALL TOURNAMENT?

AIN'T YOU LISTENIN' TO YORE RADIO, LADY? STUMPHILL BEAT WEST OLEANDREA AN' WE'RE LICKIN' OBERDEEN RIGHT NOW! — I'M GOIN' BACK TO TH' SET — LIKE EVERY OTHER STUMPHILL WORKIN' STIFF OL' COP-PERHEAD CALHOON WOULDN'T LET OFF T' GO TO THE GAMES!

CLICK!

MILTON CANIFF

OBERDEEN TRIES FOR A DRIVE IN UN--- AND THERE'S THE GUN! STUMPHILL WINS, 52-49!

AND OBERDEEN WAS THE CLASS OF THE LEAGUE THIS YEAR! WHAT'S GOT INTO THOSE MINERS?

MAYBE THAT GIRL COACH HAS 'EM HENPECKED INTO THE UPPER INCOME BRACKET!

NEXT DAY...

SUMMER! HOW DID COPPER HAPPEN TO LET YOU OFF AGAIN?

SHE THINKS WE ARE MISERABLE TOGETHER, STEVE!

THIS IS THE SEMI-FINAL IN B DIVISION OF THE FOURTH DISTRICT ELIM-INATIONS!

IF THIS DARKHORSE STUMPHILL TEAM WITH ITS COWGIRL COACH CAN GET BY NEWBRIDGE TODAY, IT WILL FACE ITS REAL TEST AGAINST MT. IVY TONIGHT!

LONDON OPAIRATOR, MEES CAL-HOON SAYS SHE CANNOT COME TO THE TELEPHONE BECAUSE STOMPHEEL EES CLOBBAIREENG MONT EYE-VEE!.. WHATEVAIR THAT MEANS!

NOW I KNOW ALL AMAIREE-CANS ARE NOTS!

MILTON CANIFF

STEVE, I WOULD KNOW HOW TO HANDLE THIS IN THE CITY, BUT I'M LOST! COPPER WANTS TICKETS FOR THE STATE BASKETBALL TOURNAMENT!

THIS MAY SURPRISE YOU, SUMMER, BUT POTEET LEFT HER OWN TWO SEATS FOR YOU AND COPPER!

LATER

MEES CALHOON, EES DETECTEEV TO PROTECT THE BODY!

ELI BUSH IS THE NAME, MA'AM! I'M TO LOOK AFTER YOU DURING THE BASKETBALL TOURNAMENT!

ARE YOU CRAZY? I DON'T NEED A STRONGARM BOY! GET OUT!

BEGGIN' YOUR PARDON, MA'AM, BUT WE HAD AN—AH—PHONE CALL FROM SOMEBODY THREATENING YOU WHILST AT THE TOURNAMENT!

SORRY TO BE A BOTHER, MA'AM, BUT MY BOSS SENT ME TO GUARD YOU —AN' I NEED MY JOB!

ONLY STEVE AND POTEET KNOW WE ARE GOING TO THE TOURNAMENT! —AND HE WOULD HARDLY HAVE MADE THAT CALL!

LOOK! THAT'S COPPER CALHOON! I NEVER THOUGHT I'D SEE HER STANDING UP WAITING TO CHEER THE STUMPHILL TEAM AS IT COMES ON THE FLOOR!

DON'T KID YOURSELF!.. SHE'S PROBABLY COUNTING THE HOUSE!

3-10

OLSON, THESE ARE QUITE DECENT SEATS! —WHO'S OUR BROKER?

THESE ARE POTEET CANYON'S TICKETS —WHICH SHE LEFT FOR US TO USE, MISS CALHOON!

HOW TOUCHING! —AND THE POLICE SENT A BODYGUARD! —MY CUP RUNNETH OVER!

THERE SEEM TO BE SO FEW PEOPLE FROM STUMPHILL HERE TO SUPPORT THE TEAM!

WE FLEW TO THAT AWFUL TOWN TO HELP INCREASE PRODUCTION! YOU DON'T THINK I GAVE ANYONE THE DAY OFF, DO YOU?

N-NO, MA'AM!

WHILE BACK IN THE STUMPHILL MINE...

ABOUT READY TO GO ON THE FIRST ROUND! THE OPENER IS STUMPHILL AGAINST NAYLORVILLE...

Y'MEAN YOU GOT AN OKAY TO PIPE THE GAME INTO THE LOUD-SPEAKER?

RIGHT! MISS CALHOON'S SECRETARY CAME OVER PERSONALLY TO SEE THAT IT WAS DONE!

DAVE, YOU GET A BREAK EVERY YEAR, BEING ABLE TO SCOUT TALENT RIGHT IN YOUR OWN GYM! WHICH OF THE CURRENT CROP OF HIGH SCHOOL HOT ROCKS IS STATE ROMANCING?

WE'RE JUST PORE OL' PUBLIC SCHOOL TYPES, BERT! YOU ENDOWED COLLEGE DUDES COME HERE WITH POCKETS FULL OF SCHOLARSHIPS —AND WE HAVE TO TAKE THE LEAVINGS!

OH, SURE! IT'S RUMORED THAT YOU TRIED TO CORNER THESE STUMPHILL KIDS AND SELL THEM ON STATE— BUT THE GIRL COACH DIDN'T KNOW YOU WERE THE GREAT HOOK DAVIDSON AND ORDERED YOU TO LEAVE THE DORM!

I HEARD THAT HOOK THEN TRIED TO SIGN THE CANYON DOLL ON AS HIS OWN ASSISTANT, SO SHE WOULD BRING THE STUMPHILL SQUAD WITH HER...

WELL, ONE MINUTE TO GO! NAYLORVILLE WILL NEVER CATCH THOSE MINERS NOW!

AND TO THINK THAT GIRL STUDENT BROUGHT THIS TEAM ALONG TO THIS POINT! I TELL YOU, THE AMATEURS WILL RUIN OUR BUSINESS YET!

3/13

M-MISS CALHOON, I CAN'T STAND IT... I GUESS I WANT STUMPHILL TO WIN SO BADLY I'M AFRAID I'LL BE ILL!.. PLEASE EXCUSE ME!

WHAT A PANTY-WAIST YOU ARE, OLSON! GO STROLL THE CAMPUS! I'LL SEND OUT A CARRIER PIGEON WITH THE SCORE!

AND SUMMER DOES JUST THAT... SHE WALKS THE NEARLY DESERTED STREETS OF THE UNIVERSITY TOWN —AS THE RAW MARCH WIND BRINGS SOUNDS OF CHEERING FROM THE GYMNASIUM ...

PARDON ME, MISTER —DO YOU KNOW THE SCORE OF THE STUMP-HILL—TRAYFIELD BASKETBALL GAME ?

THERE'S THE ANSWER, SUMMER! NOW WILL YOU JOIN ME IN A HAND-FUL OF TRANQUILIZER PILLS TO SEE IF WE CAN LAST THROUGH THE SEMI-FINALS ?... IT MUST HAVE BEEN LIKE THIS AT FORT McHENRY THE NIGHT FRANCIS SCOTT KEY WROTE THE SONG!

STEVE!

WORTHINGTON

STUMPHILL 52
TRAYFIELD 48

3/14

NOW THE CROWD TEMPERATURE REACHES A NEAR-HYSTERICAL PITCH AS POTEET SWITCHES STRATEGY TO BOX THE EXTRA TALL BOY ON THE RIVAL TEAM IN THE SEMI-FINAL TOURNAMENT GAME

HE ALWAYS FEEDS TO THE REDHEAD — #31! STOP DOUBLE-TEAMING TH' BIG BOY AN' COVER HIS PAL!... GO, MAN!

IT'S AN ODD THING THAT NO TEAM UP TO NOW HAS THOUGHT OF LEAVING BIG APPLETON ALONE! THE LAD CAN'T SEEM TO DRIBBLE—AND HIS SET SHOTS ARE SHAKY—

HE FINALLY PASSES TO THE PLAYMAKER, #31, BUT ONE OF THE TWO STUMPHILL MEN GUARDING 31 INTERCEPTS AND DRIVES DOWN THE COURT, USING THAT LOW-ANGLE DRIBBLE WHICH HAS SERVED THEM SO WELL...

S.F.D.

THE WORTHINGTON TEAM WAS NOT ABLE TO SWITCH ITS ATTACK IN TIME TO BREAK THE STUMPHILL DEFENSE! THERE'S THE GUN!... AND THE IN-CREDIBLE SIX-MAN SQUAD WITH ITS COWGIRL STUDENT-COACH GOES INTO THE FINALS OF THIS 1957 STATE TOURNAMENT...

STEVE CANYON

THERE IS NO EXCITEMENT QUITE LIKE PUBLIC REACTION TO A DARK-HORSE TEAM WHICH GETS HOT IN A STATE HIGH SCHOOL BASKETBALL TOURNAMENT!...STUMPHILL HAS FOUGHT THROUGH THE ELIMINATION GAMES —— AND NOW...

STUMPHILL SCHOOL VERSUS VALLEY ACADEMY FOR THE B DIVISION CHAMPIONSHIP!

WHAT HAVE THOSE KIDS GOT? THEY'RE AS POISED AS PROFESSIONALS!

YET THEY DIDN'T WIN A GAME ALL SEASON!

THEY HAVE COLOR! THAT GIRL STUDENT-COACH WOULD BE ENOUGH, BUT THEY ALSO HAVE ONLY SIX PLAYERS ON THE SQUAD!

STEVE, HOW DID YOU TALK ME INTO COMING TO THIS THING? I'M SO WORKED UP I'M AFRAID TO WATCH!

POTEET IS AS CALM DOWN THERE AS IF SHE WERE CONDUCTING A KINDERGARTEN GAME PERIOD

OLSON, WHY DIDN'T YOU TELL ME THIS HIGH-SCHOOL BASKETBALL WAS SO EXHILARATING?

WHY—AH—I NEVER THOUGHT OF IT, MISS CALHOON...

3-17

3/20

THE STUMPHILL TEAM USES EVERY TRICK LEARNED FROM THE BIG THUNDER AIR-MEN, BUT THE VALLEY ACADEMY IS AT ITS PEAK FOR THIS GAME — AND THE SLIM LEAD SHIFTS BACK AND FORTH

THE TENSION RISES BY THE MINUTE!

THE BODY CONTACT UNDER THE BASKETS IS CLEAN BUT BRUISING AS THE PLAYERS FIGHT FOR THE REBOUNDS...

..TWO FREE THROWS BY VALLEY TIES THE SCORE AS THE HALF ENDS...

HOW DO YOU MAKE IT, KEN?

STUMPHILL HAS TWO MEN CHARGED WITH THREE PERSONAL FOULS EACH!

3/21

AT HALF TIME THE NEWS OF THE MINE DISASTER AT STUMPHILL QUICKLY SPREADS THROUGH THE CROWD

HEY! THERE WAS AN EXPLOSION AT THE STUMPHILL MINE... THAT MUST BE WHY THE ONE KID LEFT!

THEY'RE SAYING OUTSIDE THAT THE WHOLE NIGHT SHIFT WAS CAUGHT UNDERGROUND BECAUSE THAT CALHOON DAME WHO OWNS THE MINE WOULDN'T GIVE THE MEN TIME OFF TO COME TO THE TOURNAMENT!

WOW! I'LL BET SHE'LL HAVE A CONSCIENCE! PROBABLY ON SOME WILD PARTY IN PARIS OR NEW YORK RIGHT NOW!

WHAT A FIEND THAT HAG MUST BE!

ROSCOE, I SAW A PICTURE IN THE PAPERS... AND I HAVE A HORRIBLE SUSPICION...

SAVE IT, HONEY— HERE COME THE TEAMS!

STEVE CANYON
by MILTON CANIFF

THE BOY WHOSE FATHER WAS IN THE SHAFT DURING THE STUMP-HILL MINE EXPLOSION HAS HURRIED HOME — BUT AT HIS INSISTENCE, THE TEAM STAYS ON TO PLAY FOR THE CHAMPIONSHIP! IT IS THE FINAL PERIOD AND THE SCORE IS TIED...

THE TEAMS ARE PLAYING HARD, SHARP BASKETBALL — ONE MISTAKE AND THE OTHER SIDE SCORES! THEN, AS VALLEY ACADEMY DRIVES IN TO BREAK THE DEADLOCK ...

OH-H-H, THERE'S A WHISTLE!

WOW-W! — I HATE TO DO THIS... BUT IT'S WHAT I'M PAID FOR!...

HOLDING!

THAT'S THE FIFTH PERSONAL FOUL ON KRUSE! HE'S OUT OF THE GAME!....

OFFICIAL'S TIME OUT

STUMPHILL HAS NO SUBSTITUTES!

BUT THE TEAM MUST GO ON WITH FOUR MEN!

I – I'LL BET THOSE STUMPHILL KIDS CAN STILL WIN WITH ONLY FOUR PLAYERS!

YOU'RE OUT OF YOUR MIND! NAME YOUR PRICE! — YOU'RE COVERED!

M-MISS CALHOON... YOU MEAN YOU'D BET AGAINST STUMPHILL SCHOOL?

A BET'S A BET! HOW MUCH WILL YOU PUT ON STUMPHILL TO WIN?

WH– WHY, I --

HERE'S FIVE HUNDRED DOLLARS THAT SAYS YOU'RE WRONG!

MISS CALHOON, YOU'RE UNDER ARREST FOR MAKING A MONEY BET WHILE ON STATE UNIVERSITY PROPERTY!

3-24

I AM WHAT, YOU CLOD?

MISS CALHOON, I SAID YOU ARE UNDER ARREST FOR MAKING A MONEY BET ON STATE UNIVERSITY PROPERTY. YOU MUST HAVE FORGOTTEN THAT YOUR BODYGUARD IS A STATE POLICE PLAINCLOTHESMAN!

I WILL CONFISCATE AS EVIDENCE THAT $500 YOU WERE BETTING ON VALLEY ACADEMY! YOU WITNESSES WILL PLEASE GIVE ME YOUR NAMES!

OLSON! GET MY LAWYERS ON THE PHONE —FAST!

—AND, MRS. OLSON, YOU'D BETTER FIND SOME BAIL MONEY! —WE CLODS TAKE OUR ANTI-GAMBLING LAWS ABSURDLY SERIOUSLY!

POTEET SENT US THESE RESERVED SEATS —AND THE BODYGUARD CAME AFTER AN ANONYMOUS TELEPHONED THREAT... THE CHILD GUESSED THAT COPPER DIDN'T KNOW THE LAW AND WOULD TRY TO BET ON THE GAME —POTEET, FOR THIS YOU DESERVE TO WIN A NATIONAL CHAMPIONSHIP!

STUMPHILL HAS ONLY FOUR ELIGIBLE PLAYERS! CAN THEY CONTINUE?

THE RULES SAY YOU MUST START WITH FIVE, BUT YOU CAN STAY IN THE GAME WITH LESS THAN FIVE!

STUMPHILL CAPTAIN, READY TO PLAY?

YES, SIR

MISTER REFEREE...

...SINCE STUMPHILL HAS NO SUBSTITUTES TO SEND IN...

...OUR VALLEY ACADEMY PLAYERS HAVE VOTED TO ASK THAT THEIR LAST MAN NOT BE SENT OUT! KEEP IT AN EVEN GAME!

91

3/29

VALLEY IS AHEAD BY ONE LONE POINT AS STUMPHILL'S CENTER CALMLY PREPARES TO TAKE TWO FREE THROWS AFTER BEING FOULED...

ONE! —AND THE SCORE IS TIED...

TWO! AND STUMPHILL LEADS BY A POINT...

VALLEY HURRIEDLY PUTS THE BALL BACK INTO PLAY...

—AND THE VALLEY GUARD SEES THE TIME- KEEPER'S GUN BEING RAISED! HE SHOOTS FROM THE CENTER OF THE COURT, AS STUMP- HILL HAS BEEN DOING! —WHILE THE BALL IS IN MIDAIR, THE CRACK OF THE PISTOL SOUNDS ABOVE THE ROAR OF THE CROWD!

3/30

THE TIMEKEEPER'S GUN FIRES AS THE BALL IS IN FLIGHT... IT HITS THE BASKET CLEANLY — AND VALLEY ACADEMY WINS BY ONE POINT!...

FOR A SPLIT SECOND THERE IS AN UNBELIEVING SILENCE — THEN THE CROWD ROARS —

AT THIS POINT STEVE CANYON DRIVES UP TO THE GYM...

THE NEW B DIVISION STATE CHAMPIONS...

...VALLEY ACADEMY!

OLSON, PUT UP THE STUPID BAIL!... I WOULD HAVE WON THE BET... OH, FOR HEAVEN'S SAKE, WHAT ARE YOU BAWLING ABOUT?

93

STEVE CANYON

MILTON CANIFF

FINISHING THE FINAL GAME WITH ONLY FOUR PLAYERS IS TOO MUCH OF A HANDICAP EVEN FOR AN INSPIRED STUMPHILL TEAM... IN THE LAST SECONDS OF PLAY, THEY LOSE — BY ONE POINT....

THE FOUR STUMPHILL BOYS ARE SURROUNDED, BUT IGNORED, BY THE TRIUMPHANT VALLEY ACADEMY CROWD

THE PLAYER WHO WENT OUT ON FOULS SITS SOBBING ON THE BENCH —POTEET CANYON TRIES TO COMFORT HIM ...

D-DON'T CRY, H-HERSCHEL... WE PLAYED GOOD — REAL GOOD!

BUT--IF -- I'DA STAYED---IN---WE ---COULDA MADE IT...

WE'LL DO IT NEXT TIME!

M-MISS POTEET, THERE WILL NEVER B-BE A SECOND CHANCE F-FOR US KIDS FROM STUMPHILL!

POTEET, YOU CAN'T GO TO THE LOCKER ROOM WITH YOUR TEAM, SO LET'S WALK OUTSIDE WHILE THE BOYS DRESS

" AFTER FOUR YEARS OF ARDUOUS SERVICE MARKED BY UNSURPASSED COURAGE AND FORTITUDE, THE ARMY OF NORTHERN VIRGINIA HAS BEEN COMPELLED TO YIELD TO OVERWHELMING NUMBERS AND RESOURCES...

"...I NEED NOT TELL THE BRAVE SURVIVORS OF SO MANY HARD-FOUGHT BATTLES WHO HAVE REMAINED STEADFAST TO THE LAST, THAT I HAVE CONSENTED TO THIS RESULT FROM NO DISTRUST OF THEM...

"...WITH AN UNCEASING ADMIRATION OF YOUR CONSTANCY AND DEVOTION... AND A GRATEFUL REMEMBRANCE OF YOUR KIND AND GENEROUS CONSIDERATION FOR MYSELF, I BID YOU ALL AN AFFECTIONATE FAREWELL..."

WH-WHAT IS THAT, COUSIN STEVIE?

IT'S FROM GENERAL ROBERT E. LEE'S FAREWELL ORDER TO HIS TROOPS! WHEN YOU THINK HOW HE MUST HAVE FELT AT THAT MOMENT— IT ALWAYS MAKES ANY LOST FIGHT SEEM A LITTLE LESS LIKE THE END OF THE WORLD...

3-31

NOW THAT YOU HAVE HAD YOUR FUN, I PRESUME I MAY GO!

YES, SINCE YOU POSTED BAIL, MISS CALHOON, YOU ARE AT LIBERTY TO LEAVE UNTIL YOUR HEARING ON CHARGES OF MAKING A MONEY BET ON STATE UNIVERSITY PROPERTY

ISN'T MY FEARLESS BODYGUARD — WHO ALSO ARRESTED ME FOR GAMBLING — GOING TO ESCORT US HOME?

HE WAS ASSIGNED FOR THE DURATION OF THE TOURNAMENT, MA'AM!

MRS. OLSON BROUGHT A LARGE SUM OF CASH MONEY TO COVER MY BAIL... I DEMAND CONTINUING POLICE PROTECTION!

I'LL ASSIGN ANOTHER MAN, MISS CALHOON! I'M NOT GOING TO GIVE YOU A CHANCE TO WORK TROOPER BUSH OVER THE COALS ALL THE WAY FROM HERE TO YOUR HOUSE!

POTEET, HONEY, I'M SO SORRY YOUR TEAM LOST... BUT BOTH SIDES CAN'T WIN!

Y-YES, MRS. TORR, BUT W-WHY DID IT HAVE T'BE US WHO LOST?

SOME SLEEP WILL MAKE IT ALL SEEM LESS MISERABLE, DEAR...

I'LL GO TO THE OTHER TRAILER AND FIX YOU SOME WARM MILK!

MRS. TORR IS SWEET AN' GENTLE AN' KINDLY — AN' I LOVE HER VERY DEEPLY...

...BUT SHE PROBABLY WOULDA TOLD NATHAN HALE THAT SOMEBODY HAD TO BE HUNG SO WE SCHOOL KIDS WOULD HAVE THINGS TO QUOTE!

POTEET, CALL WHEN YOU'RE READY AND I'LL TUCK YOU IN...

YOU WEREN'T LONG! NO BEAUTY CREAM OR HAIR CURLERS?

YOU'RE BUILDIN' ME UP T' SOUND LIKE A GLAMOUR TYPE, COUSIN STEVIE... AND I'M RIGHT PLEASED! —BUT I KNOW YOU'RE JUST TRYIN' T' JOLLY ME...

OKAY—THEN YOU'RE JUST A PUG-NOSED LITTLE TOWHEAD FROM TEXAS WHO'S TEED OFF BECAUSE YOU MISSED THE GLORY ROAD BY ONE LOUSY POINT...

...AND WHY DIDN'T TWO GUYS ON THE OTHER TEAM BREAK A LEG? —DOES THAT FIT?

YOU SHAME ME 'CAUSE YOU'RE RIGHT— BUT YOU PLEASE ME BY NOT TREATIN' ME LIKE A PANTY-WAIST!

HOW DID POTEET SLEEP, MRS. TORR?

STEVE, I'M A LITTLE CONCERNED! —SHE WAS UP AND GONE BEFORE I OPENED MY EYES!

OLSON! WHERE ARE YOU GOING?

WHY—AH—THE DOOR SEEMS TO BE STANDING OPEN, MISS CALHOON!

MISS MAID, IT'S POTEET CANYON COME T' CONFESS SOMETHING T' MISS CALHOON!

IF THAT IS WHO IT SOUNDS LIKE, TELL HER TO GO AWAY! I SHALL PUNISH SUMMER OLSON FOR THE THINGS THE BRAT DID TO ME!

STEVE CANYON

MILTON CANIFF

WHO'S THERE?

MISS CALHOON —IT'S POTEET CANYON

GET AWAY FROM ME, YOU CONNIVING LITTLE RAT! YOU MADE A SUCKER OUT OF ME! I AM OUT ON BAIL RIGHT THIS MINUTE!

YOU LURED ME INTO COMING HERE, THEN CONNED ME INTO GOING TO THAT BASKET-BALL TOURNA-MENT!

YOU KNEW I'D GET WORKED UP AND COVER A BET, WHICH IS AGAINST THE LAW ON STATE UNIVERSITY PROPERTY!

YES, MA'AM, I DID EXACTLY THAT, BE-CAUSE YOU WERE SO MEAN TO MRS. OLSON!—AFTER SHE SO KINDLY SENT US THE BASKETBALL UNIFORMS!

I DID A BAD THING —AND I CAME TO TELL YOU I'M SORRY!

DID YOUR COUSIN STEVE PUT YOU UP TO THIS?

OH, NO, MA'AM! HE DOESN'T KNOW ANYTHING ABOUT WHAT I DID!

I WANTED TO HURT YOU, MISS CALHOON! IT WAS A SINFUL THING — AND I WAS PUNISHED BY LOSIN' THE TOURNAMENT!

I SOLD MY DRESSES AN' BROUGHT YOU THE MONEY TO PAY PART OF YOUR FINE! I'LL SEND YOU THE REST FROM MY BABY-SITTIN' WAGES!

IF I TOOK YOUR MONEY YOU COULD BRAG AROUND ABOUT YOUR GREAT SACRIFICE

OLSON! — SEND THIS CHILD AWAY — AND PACK MY THINGS! WE'RE LEAVING THIS MISERABLE PLACE!

I'M SO SORRY POTEET, DEAR

TH-THAT'S ALL RIGHT... ...MRS. OLSON... I'M REAL OBLIGED TO YOU... FOR THE KINDLY THINGS YOU DID FOR US...

OLSON, IF YOU WALK OUT THAT DOOR YOUR INVALID HUSBAND, YOUR SON AND YOU WILL BE BACK ON RELIEF!

4-7

100

POTEET, WE WERE WORRIED! ARE YOU ALL RIGHT?

COUSIN STEVIE, YOU VERY KINDLY DIDN'T ASK ME WHERE I'VE BEEN, SO I'M GONNA TELL YOU!

I WENT TO MISS CALHOON'S HOUSE TO TELL HER I HAD PLOTTED RIGHT SINFUL TO HAVE HER ARRESTED FOR GAMBLING!

I OFFERED TO PAY HER FINE, BUT SHE THREW ME OUT!... NOW, SIR, I'VE GOT A REQUEST T'MAKE OF YOU...

THAT UNKINDLY WOMAN IS LEAVING STUMP-HILL RIGHT AWAY!.. HER AIRPLANE IS STILL PARKED HERE AT BIG THUNDER... AND IF YOU DON'T DO SOMETHING ABOUT SAVIN' MISSUS OLSON FROM SUCH A WITCH — I WILL!

YES, COL. CANYON! MISS CALHOON NOTIFIED US THAT SHE WILL DEPART BIG THUNDER IN HER AIRCRAFT AT ONCE...

...IN FACT HER NEW PILOT AND COPILOT ARE WAITING HERE NOW!

YOU'RE RIGHT, POTEET! COPPER AND SUMMER ARE LEAVING!

COUSIN STEVIE, ARE YOU GONNA RESCUE THAT WRETCHY MISSUS OLSON — OR MUST I?

SUMMER STAYS WITH COPPER CALHOON SO HER INVALID HUSBAND MAY GET THE BEST MEDICAL CARE — AND HER SON MAY HAVE THE BEST SCHOOLING! HOW CAN YOU RESCUE SOMEONE WHO DOESN'T WISH TO BE LIBERATED?

COURSE NOT, IF SHE'S GONE! BUT THE POLICE WILL BE RIGHT INTERESTED TO KNOW A WOMAN OUT ON BAIL IS ABOUT TO FLY OVER THE STATE LINE!!

UNKNOWN ADMIRER

APRIL 13 to
JUNE 9, 1957

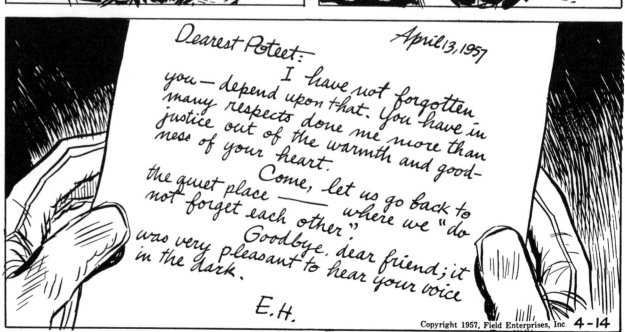

April 16, 1957

Poteet, dearest:— It could have been said of you that — "She untied her hat and let the damp hair fall... She put my arm about her waist — and made her smooth white shoulder bare, ...all her yellow hair displaced, and, stooping, made my cheek lie there — and spread o'er all, her yellow hair..."

E.H.

GEE!.. I MEAN... WOOHOO! —ZOWEEEE!

LATER

TORRY, HAVE YOU SEEN POTEET? SHE DASHED IN FROM SCHOOL, PICKED UP A LETTER THAT CAME FOR HER, THEN DISAPPEARED!

I SAW HER OVER IN THE BASE EXCHANGE STARING AT EVERY JOKER WHO PASSED BY! MAYBE THOSE LETTERS SHE'S BEEN GETTING ARE FROM A CORRESPONDENCE COURSE ON HOW TO BE A LADY DETECTIVE!

MILTON CANIFF

POTEET, WHAT ARE YOU DOING?

WHY — AH — I THOUGHT I'D PRESS MY WHITE DRESS WITH THE JACKET! IT'S ALL RIGHT, ISN'T IT, MRS. TORR?

OF COURSE, DEAR! I WAS SURPRISED BECAUSE I HADN'T SEEN YOU — AH — DOING ANY PRESSING BEFORE!

YOU **FEEL** ALL RIGHT, DON'T YOU, POTEET?

OH, YES, MRS. TORR! I FEEL FINE!

MILTON CANIFF

AS THE MOTHER OF GROWING GIRLS I HAVE BEGUN TO DREAD THE COMING OF SPRING!

108

COUSIN STEVE B., HOW DO THEY KEEP TRACK OF ALL THE PEOPLE ON A BASE LIKE BIG THUNDER?

MILES OF PAPER WORK, POTEET!... THE MEN ARE ALWAYS FILLING OUT SOME NEW FORM OR OTHER!

I'D JUS' LOVE TO SEE SOME OF THOSE RECORDS! I MIGHT BE ABLE TO WRITE A THEME ON THEM FOR SCHOOL!

IT WOULD BE AN INVASION OF PRIVACY TO ALLOW AN UN-AUTHORIZED PERSON TO LOOK AT THE MEN'S OWN STATEMENTS..

SCHOOL BUS STOP

MILTON CANIFF

BUT I'M SURE ONE OF THE BOYS WOULD BE GLAD TO TYPE OUT AN UNCLASSIFIED CROSS-SECTION BREAKDOWN OF THE AIRMEN AND THEIR JOBS!

OH..

TORRY, I DON'T THINK STEVE IS AWARE THAT POTEET HAS BEEN GETTING A LETTER IN THE MAIL EVERY DAY...

WHAT'S WRONG WITH THAT?

NOTHING—EXCEPT THAT SHE REACTS TO EACH ONE AS IF IT WERE FROM HER FAVORITE MOVIE STAR!

BUT SHE NEVER SEEMS TO ANSWER! —IT'S A ONE-WAY CORRESPONDENCE!

MILTON CANIFF

WHY DON'T YOU TAKE A PEEK AT ONE OF HER NOTES?

TORRY! THAT WOULD HARDLY BE GOOD MANNERS!

...AND BESIDES — SHE KEEPS THEM LOCKED IN A BOX IN HER SUITCASE!

EVERY DAY SINCE HER TEAM LOST THE BASKET-BALL TOURNAMENT, POTEET HAS RECEIVED AN UNSIGNED LETTER IN THE MAIL...

OH!

HI, KITTEN!

WELL, POTEET, NOW THAT BASKETBALL IS FINISHED, THE STUMP-HILL STUDENTS WILL BE WANTING A BASEBALL TEAM...

I RECKON SO, COUSIN STEVIE B.,

WILL THEY BE AFTER YOU TO COACH THE SQUAD?

I DON'T RIGHTLY KNOW, SIR!

WAS THERE A TELEPHONE CALL FOR ME, MRS. TORR?

NO, POTEET

THEN IF Y'ALL WILL EXCUSE ME, I HAVE SOME THINGS T'DO IN THE OTHER TRAILER...

POTEET IS IN LOVE!

THAT'S A BIG STATEMENT, EVEN FOR YOU, MRS. T.

THIS IS THE FIRST TIME I HAVE SEEN HER WEAR HER DRESSES INSTEAD OF THE JEANS! BUT WHERE IS THE BOY SHE'S SHOWING OFF FOR?

AS STEVE AND THE TORRS SPECULATE, POTEET JUST 'HAPPENS' TO BE AT THE MAILBOX WHEN THE DELIVERY IS MADE...

WHEN THE POSTMAN DELIVERS THE DAY'S MAIL TO THE TORR LETTER BOX, POTEET IS WAITING

WELL, WHADYA KNOW! THERE'S ANOTHER ONE FOR YOU, MISS CANYON!

SIR, I'D BE OBLIGED IF YOU WOULDN'T TELL MAJOR AND MRS. TORR THAT I'VE BEEN GETTING LETTERS...THEY-AH-THINK IT'S A WASTE OF TIME FOR ME TO ENTER CONTESTS...

BUT YOUR LETTERS HAVE ALL BEEN IN THE SAME HAND-WRITING, POTEET! WHAT KIND OF CONTE---

OH, I ENTER THROUGH AN-AH-AGENT! COL. CANYON MIGHT NOT LIKE IT IF I WON AND IT SOUNDED LIKE AN ENDORSEMENT, COMING FROM AN AIR FORCE DEPENDENT!

POTEET WAITS UNTIL THE POSTMAN DRIVES ON....THEN TEARS OPEN THE ENVELOPE... SO NERVOUS SHE IS SHAKING...

113

HMM—PART OF A LETTER... CAN'T TELL WHO IT'S ADDRESSED TO! GUESS I'LL _HAVE_ TO READ IT TO FIND OUT WHOSE IT IS...

no surprise; I thought from the beginning it was too good to last, and felt as one does in a garden one has entered by an open door—people fancy you mean to steal flowers.

I left you always to decide (as only _yourself_ could) on what length into the garden I might go: and I still leave it to you....Two persons who sudden-ly unclasp arms and start off in opposite directions look terrib-ly intimate. But you know all

WOW!

THIS IS NO KID STUFF! SOME ADULT MALE IS WRITING TO POTEET!

SHOULD I TELL STEVE? THERE ARE HUNDREDS OF MEN ON THIS BASE NOW...

WHICH ONE IS IT?

4-28

STEVE, WHAT DISTURBS ME IS THAT MY YOUNG SON HANGS AROUND HERE EVERY LEISURE MINUTE HE HAS. I DON'T WANT EVEN MY OWN CHILD TO GET IN YOUR HAIR!

IS *THAT* ALL?

DON'T GIVE IT ANOTHER THOUGHT, MAYOR STRAAW! UNTIL THE AIR FORCE NEEDS THAT LAND, BIG THUNDER KIDS ARE WELCOME TO IT AS A PLAYGROUND!

STRANGE MAN, THAT MAYOR STRAAW...EVEN THE YOUNG SON IS AN INTERESTING EGO MANIFESTATION! I'M AFRAID THEY DON'T HAVE MUCH FUN TOGETHER!

NOT MANY PARENTS SEEM TO PAL AROUND WITH THEIR CHILDREN *THESE* DAYS!

COL. CANYON, IT'S MAJOR IRVING WITH A REPORT!

AH! THE HANDWRITING TEST! *NOW* WE'LL FIND OUT WHO HAS BEEN SENDING THOSE LETTERS TO POTEET!

LET'S HAVE IT, IRV. WHO WROTE THE LETTER?

WELL, STEVE, WE'RE NOT THE F.B.I., BUT FROM THE FAST HAND-WRITING CHECK WE RAN THERE CAN ONLY BE ONE CONCLUSION...

WELL?...

IT WASN'T ANYONE ON THIS BASE!

MEANWHILE...

HERE'S YOUR LETTER, POTEET! RIGHT ON THE DOT!

May 1, 1957

Poteet, my own = I feel as if I had been close, so close, to some world's wonder in chapel or crypt. I might have entered, but there is always some slight and just sufficient bar restraining me from presenting my-self to you. The half-opened door shuts and I must go my thousands of miles away from you for another day, my dearest.

E.H.

118

119

STEVE CANYON
by MILTON CANIFF

FOR THE FIRST TIME IN SEVERAL DAYS, POTEET CANYON HAS FAILED TO RECEIVE AN ARDENT LOVE LETTER FROM HER UNKNOWN ADMIRER....

MEANWHILE

STEVE, I WOULDN'T HAVE RECOGNIZED FROM THIS ONE SHEET OF HANDWRITING THAT POTEET'S BEAU WAS COPYING THE LOVE LETTERS OF ROBERT BROWNING, THE POET!

WE KNOW LITTLE MORE THAN THAT ABOUT HIM, HOWEVER!

OUR SECURITY PEOPLE CHECKED THE HAND-WRITING WITH THAT OF EVERY MAN ON THE BASE... ALL NEGATIVE!

COULD IT BE SOMEONE IN STUMPHILL?

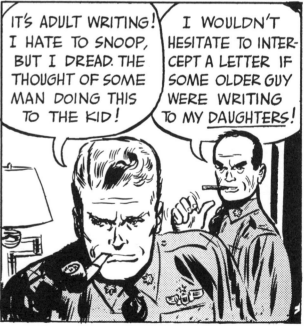

IT'S ADULT WRITING! I HATE TO SNOOP, BUT I DREAD. THE THOUGHT OF SOME MAN DOING THIS TO THE KID!

I WOULDN'T HESITATE TO INTER-CEPT A LETTER IF SOME OLDER GUY WERE WRITING TO MY DAUGHTERS!

121

WELL, AT LEAST POTEET IS TALKING TO SOMEONE HER OWN AGE —

INSTEAD OF MOONING OVER THOSE LETTERS FROM AN OLDER GUY

WHO IS THAT SHE'S WITH ?

IT'S EDDIE STRAAW, SON OF THE MAYOR! — KIND OF AN ODD BALL! HE'S ON THE BASE WITH THE BIG THUNDER TOWN LEAGUE BALL TEAMS — ALTHOUGH HE DOESN'T SEEM TO PLAY !

COLONEL CANYON AND MAJOR TORR SEEM SATISFIED THAT IT IS THE SON OF MAYOR STRAAW TALKING WITH YOU, POTEET !

HEEHEE ! WOULDN'T THEY CALL OUT THE GUARD IF THEY KNEW IT WAS I WHO WROTE YOU THE LOVE LETTERS ?

THIS IS THE FIRST TIME I HAVE EVER SEEN YOU SPEECHLESS !

WELL, EDDIE STRAAW, THE JOKE'S ON ME !

OH, IT WAS NO JOKE, POTEET ! I AM NOT A SKILLED AUTHOR, SO I PARAPHRASED ONLY THE FINEST LOVE LETTERS TO SEND YOU...

THEY WERE THE WORK OF ROBERT BROWNING, THE POET !

DO TELL ! I HOPE MR. BROWNING WOULD BE PROUD THAT I FELL FOR HIS WOOIN' TALK !

WHY DID YOU SIGN THE LETTERS "E.H." ?

THAT STANDS FOR "EDDIE HIMSELF"

124

126

FIRST I USED PLAIN STATIONERY, PENS AND INK BOUGHT AT THE BASE EXCHANGE!

THEN I WORE RUBBER GLOVES...

I HAD PHOTOSTATED FINGERPRINTS FROM THE BIG THUNDER PISTOL-PERMIT FILES, WHICH I COULD 'BORROW' BECAUSE MY FATHER IS MAYOR OF THE TOWN!

I ETCHED THOSE PRINTS ONTO THIN STRIPS OF RUBBER WHICH I CEMENTED TO THE GLOVE FINGERS! THE PRINTS ON THOSE LETTERS ARE COL. CANYON'S!

WHEN THE POLICE AND THE AIR FORCE LEARN THAT HE HAS BEEN WRITING SUCH THINGS TO HIS LEGAL WARD — A MINOR — IT WILL MAKE QUITE A STORY!

HOW YOU DO TAKE ON!

I HAVE ALL THOSE LETTERS LOCKED AWAY!

YOU DID HAVE — UNTIL I TOOK THEM! NOW YOU SUSPECT YOUR COUSIN AND HAVE SENT THE MAIL TO THE POLICE BECAUSE YOU ARE AFRAID CANYON IS CRAZY AND WILL TRY TO HURT YOU!

5-19

131

POTEET, I CAME OVER ON SUNDAY MORNING WHILE YOU AND THE TORRS WERE AT CHURCH

IT WAS EASY TO OPEN YOUR BAG AND TAKE THE LETTERS SIGNED "E.H." MEANING "EDDIE HIMSELF"!

WITH MY COPIES OF COL. CANYON'S FINGERPRINTS ON EVERY PAGE, IT WILL BE EASY TO RUIN HIM IN THE AIR FORCE!

EDDIE, WHAT WILL YOUR FATHER THINK IF YOU ARE ARRESTED AS A FORGER AND BLACKMAILER?!

OH, I WON'T BE CAUGHT!.. ALTHOUGH MY ONE REGRET IS THAT FATHER WILL NEVER KNOW HOW SUCCESSFUL I HAVE BEEN —SO HE COULD BE PROUD OF ME!

EDDIE, IF I KISS YOU, WILL YOU LET ME ALONE?

OF COURSE NOT, POTEET! I WANT YOU AS MY STEADY GIRL! ANY TIME YOU TRY TO BREAK IT OFF, I'LL SEND YOUR LETTERS TO THE POLICE

WHERE DO YOU KEEP THOSE LETTERS?

OH, I MIGHT HAVE THEM RIGHT HERE IN MY POCKET!

YOU DON'T HAVE THEM!

THE MINUTE I SAID THAT, I KNEW IT WAS AN ERROR IN JUDGMENT!

132

WHAT AM I GONNA DO?

IF I DON'T KNUCKLE UNDER TO THAT EDDIE STRAAW AND HE GETS AWAY WITH TELLIN' THE POLICE THAT COUSIN STEVIE B. WROTE ME THOSE LETTERS, IT WILL BE AWFUL!

EVEN IF I DO GO STEADY WITH EDDIE, HE COULD MAKE IT ROUGH FOR COUSIN STEVE WHENEVER HE GOT SORE AT SOMETHING I DID...

BUT I'VE GOTTA STOP PUSSYFOOTIN' AROUND...

SO I'VE MADE UP MY MIND!

WHERE'S STEVE?

HE SAID HE'D HAVE DINNER ON THE BASE!

POTEET HOME?

SHE WENT OUT TO THE FILLING STATION TO MAKE HER 'PRIVATE' PHONE CALL TO EDDIE STRAAW!

HE'LL BE COMING OVER?

I IMAGINE SO!—HE USUALLY JUMPS WHEN SHE EVEN CRACKS HER KNUCKLES!

HELLO, EDDIE! I'VE DECIDED...

I CAN TELL BY YOUR TONE OF VOICE WHAT YOU MEAN!

LET ME SEE THAT PURSE! I DON'T WANT YOU RECORDING OUR CONVERSATION ON A PORTABLE MACHINE...

IT'S ONLY A PURSE!

..IF YOU ARE GOING TO BE COLD-BLOODED ABOUT THIS, WHERE ARE THE LETTERS YOU WROTE ME — WITH FAKED FINGERPRINTS OF MY COUSIN STEVIE CANYON?! OUR BARGAIN WAS THAT YOU'D GIVE THEM BACK!

NOT AT ALL! YOU WILL BE MY GIRL FROM NOW ON! AND I'LL BLACKMAIL COL. CANYON THE FIRST INSTANT YOU TRY TO GET AWAY FROM ME ...

IT SOUNDS AS IF YOU'VE GOT ME TRAPPED, EDDIE!

I KNEW I COULD NEVER INDUCE YOU TO GO STEADY WITH ME ANY OTHER WAY! — NOW KISS ME!

L-LET'S WALK OUT BY THE LAKE!.. IF A GIRL IS GOING TO BE KISSED, SHE AT LEAST WANTS IT TO SEEM ROMANTIC!

5-26

POTEET, YOU'RE A SENSIBLE GIRL! YOU MUST PLAY CHESS—YOU KNOW WHEN YOU'RE CHECKMATED!

I DON'T RIGHTLY SAVVY MUCH ABOUT THAT GAME, EDDIE, BUT I REALIZE YOU'VE GOT ME STYMIED!

NOW—ENOUGH OF THIS TALK-TALK! YOU MADE UP YOUR MIND TO ALLOW ME TO KISS YOU RATHER THAN HAVE ME BLACKMAIL COL. CANYON!

W-WELL, EDDIE, NO MATTER WHAT THE CIRCUMSTANCE—A GIRL LIKES TO BE...KINDA...COURTED!

COURTED?

YOU'VE BEEN TO THE MOVIES... TALK PRETTY TO ME AS THE ACTORS DO—SO THAT BEIN' KISSED WILL SEEM MORE —- UH—CHRON-CHRON-CHRON-O-LOGICAL!

POTEET, THIS IS NO TIME FOR BIG WORDS

YOU'RE RIGHT, EDDIE, BUT IT IS A TIME FOR SMALL ONES!

JUST BEIN' KISSED ISN'T THE WHOLE THING...IT'S THE BUILD-UP THAT'S ALMOST MORE IMPORTANT

WELL, MAYBE —BUT YOU SAID YOU'D ALLOW ME TO KISS YOU...

YES, BUT YOU HAVEN'T TOLD ME I'M PRETTY—OR COMPLIMENTED ME ABOUT MY PERFUME —OR ANYTHING...

SAY—ARE YOU TRYING TO STALL ME?

WHY, EDDIE—YOU HAVE BEEN SO SCHOLARLY ABOUT EVERYTHING ELSE IN ALL THIS—I THOUGHT YOU'D HAVE READ UP ON HOW TO MAKE LOVE!

138

BECAUSE YOU ARE THE MAYOR'S SON YOU HAD ACCESS TO THE FINGERPRINTS ON MY CITY PISTOL PERMIT, SO YOU ETCHED THEM ON RUBBER STRIPS GLUED TO RUBBER GLOVES AND LEFT WHAT SEEMED LIKE MY PRINTS ALL OVER THAT BATCH OF LOVE NOTES TO HER

THE PAPER, INK AND STAMPS WERE BOUGHT AT THE AIR BASE EXCHANGE—SO IT WOULD LOOK AS IF I HAD WRITTEN THAT STUFF TO MY WARD IN A FAKED HANDWRITING!

POTEET CAME TO ME WITH SOME LOVE LETTERS AND TOLD ME SHE WAS AFRAID COL. CANYON HAD WRITTEN THEM TO HER! SHE ASKED ME AS THE MAYOR'S SON TO HELP HER WITHOUT DISGRACING HIM!

I WAS VERY ANGRY THAT ANYONE SHOULD DO THIS TO SUCH A SWEET YOUNG LADY! I TRY POLICE LABORATORY EXPERIMENTS AS A HOBBY, SO I BROUGHT UP THE PRINTS ON THE LOVE LETTERS AND CHECKED THEM AGAINST COL. CANYON'S PISTOL PERMIT—AND SURE ENOUGH—THEY WERE HIS!

WHERE ARE THOSE LETTERS NOW, EDWARD?

THEY ARE WITH A FRIEND OF MINE WHO HAS INSTRUCTIONS TO MAIL THEM TO THE PENTAGON THE FIRST DAY HE DOESN'T HEAR FROM ME!

YOU CAN SEE THE PATTERN, DOCTOR...SLICK BEYOND HIS YEARS! BUT EDDIE OVERLOOKED ONE DETAIL...

6-2

FATHER, _YOU_ KNOW MY HOBBY IS CRIMINOLOGY! — WHEN POTEET SHOWED ME THOSE LETTERS I KNEW THEY MUST HAVE BEEN WRITTEN BY AN ADULT!

SO I CHECKED THE FINGERPRINTS WITH THE BIG THUNDER POLICE FILE AND LEARNED THEY BELONGED TO COL. STEVE CANYON!

COL. CANYON, YOU SAY MY SON MADE ONE MISTAKE IN ALL THIS?

WHEN HE ETCHED MY PRINTS FROM MY POLICE PISTOL PERMIT ON THIN RUBBER, THEN CEMENTED THEM TO THE FINGERTIPS OF THE RUBBER GLOVES

— WHICH HE WORE WHILE FORGING THAT ADULT HANDWRITING...

EDDIE ACCIDENTALLY SWITCHED THE PRINTS! ...ON THIS SHEET WE FOUND, I WOULD HAVE BEEN HOLDING THE PAPER WITH MY RIGHT HAND WHILE WRITING WITH MY LEFT!

FATHER, THIS COL. CANYON IS TRYING TO TURN SUSPICION ON ME...

...TO HIDE THE FACT THAT HE IS IN LOVE WITH POTEET!

THE VERY IDEA OF MY ETCHING HIS FINGERPRINTS ON RUBBER GLOVES TO BLACKMAIL HIM!

WHO SAID ANYTHING ABOUT BLACKMAIL, SON?

WHY — I GUESS IT WAS POTEET

SHE HASN'T SAID A WORD SINCE YOU CAME IN FROM THE LAKE!

OH, WELL — I DON'T CARE WHO IT WAS — I _COULDN'T_ HAVE MADE THE MISTAKE OF SWITCHING THOSE GLOVES AROUND — IT WAS PLANNED DOWN TO THE LAST DETAIL... I — I - TELL YOU —

SO, POTEET, WHEN YOU TOLD ME ABOUT EDDIE STRAAW AND WHAT HE WAS UP TO WE STARTED TRYING TO FIND THE HOLES IN HIS PLAN...

THE STATE POLICE LAB BROUGHT UP THE FINGER-PRINTS ON THE ONE PAGE OF HIS LETTER MRS. TORR FOUND...

...IT WAS BY ACCIDENT THAT WE LEARNED HE HAD PUT MY 'RUBBER STAMP' RIGHT-HAND PRINTS ON THE LEFT-HAND GLOVE!

YOU'RE QUIET, POTEET... AND I CAN UNDER-STAND WHY...

YES, COUSIN STEVIE...THAT WAS A RIGHT CLOSE CALL I HAD WITH POOR EDDIE...

IT WAS SO NICE GETTIN' REAL FANCY-WORDED LETTERS... I WAS STARTIN' TO BELIEVE THAT SOME GROWN MAN MIGHT ACTUALLY FALL IN LOVE WITH ME!

MILTON CANIFF

POTEET, BETWEEN BASKETBALL AND FORGERY, YOU HAVE HAD TWO ROUGH DEALS

TOMORROW, COME OVER AND HELP US INITIATE THE NEW SWIMMING POOL... IT WILL DO YOU GOOD!

MEANWHILE = ON ONE U.S. COAST

FOUR DOLLARS AND TWELVE CENTS!

AND ON THE OTHER....

MILTON CANIFF

LES, I DON'T KNOW WHO GOOFED ON THIS DEAL, BUT I WANT IT FIXED—

—BEFORE ONE OF OUR REPORTER PALS GETS THE STORY AND WE DON'T HAVE TO RE-NEW THE LEASES ON OUR WASHINGTON APARTMENTS!

STEVE CANYON by MILTON CANIFF

POOR EDDIE STRAAW!

THAT CHARACTER WAS ABOUT TO BLACKMAIL ME — AND YOU CALL HIM POOR EDDIE! WOW!

HE'S A SICK BOY, COUSIN STEVIE!

IF I HADN'T STUMBLED ON HIS BIG MISTAKE HE MIGHT HAVE HAD BOTH OF US IN A BIND!

IT WAS REAL CLEVER OF YOU TO SEE THAT HE HAD PUT THE RUBBER RE-PRODUCTIONS OF YOUR FINGERPRINTS ON THE RUBBER GLOVES IN REVERSE!

IT WOULD HAVE BEEN THE FIRST LEFT-HANDED LETTER I EVER WROTE!

POOR EDDIE IS BETTER OFF AT THE HOSPITAL HIS DAD SENT HIM TO...

DAMMA EXILE

JUNE 10 to
SEPTEMBER 24, 1957

149

HMMM!!

—HMMM!!—IN SPADES! IF ANYTHING HAPPENS TO THE HEAD OF A SMALL NATION WHILE SHE'S HERE, WE'LL LOSE MORE FRIENDS IN THAT CATEGORY...

YOU WILL BE HER 'AIDE'! SHE MUST FEEL WELCOME, BUT REMAIN OFFICIALLY INCOGNITO, SO WASHINGTON DOESN'T HAVE TO GIVE HER THE DIPLOMATIC TREATMENT JUST NOW...

SHE KNOWS YOU, SO YOU SHOULD BE ABLE TO EXPLAIN OUR POSITION!

KEEP HER OUT OF THE PUBLIC EYE—AND DON'T LET SOME RED AGENT PUSH HER IN FRONT OF A TRUCK!

IS THAT ALL?

GOOD LUCK, COL. CANYON!

MEANWHILE

... IN A CITY ON THE WEST COAST

I'M SORRY, MISS SNOW, UNLESS YOU PAY YOUR BACK RENT WE MUST ASK YOU TO GIVE UP YOUR ROOM!

Copyright 1967 Field Enterprises, Inc.   6-16

CABBY, PLEASE TELL THE GENTLEMAN THIS TAXI IS TAKEN!...

MILTON CANIFF

WHAT HAPPENED, PRINCESS?

MY MONEY WAS STOLEN! —MY AMAH AND I WERE BEING EVICTED...

I'LL PAY UP THE RENT WHILE YOU TELL YOUR AMAH EVERYTHING WILL BE OKAY...

I'M GRATEFUL —SO VERY GRATEFUL!

BIGGEST SUCKER I EVER HAULED...

WITHIN FIVE MINUTES HE MEETS THIS DOLL, SLUGS A 200-POUND SWABBIE OVER HER, PROMISES TO PAY THE BACK RENT OF HER AND HER OLD LADY —AND DOESN'T EVEN SNEAK A KISS!

...THEN TIPS ME APLENTY TO COVER MY BUSTED WINDOW!

MILTON CANIFF

TAXI

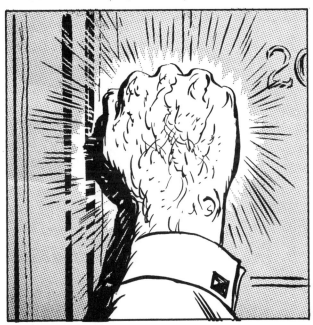

159

6/28 Copyright 1957, Field Enterprises, Inc. Registered U S Patent Office

AND THAT'S THE SCORE SO FAR, SIR! THIS MAN HOGAN SEEMS DETERMINED TO PUSH THE PRINCESS FORWARD...

..ALTHOUGH I AM NOT YET CERTAIN OF THE DETAILS!

NOT GOOD, CANYON—BUT STAY WITH IT AND KEEP US FILLED IN!

MILTON CANIFF

SO STEVE TAKES A TAXI TO PRINCESS SNOWFLOWER'S HOTEL —AND AS IT COMES TO A STOP...

OH, NO!

TAXICAB

DON'T SEEM SO SURPRISED, HOGAN! GETTING UP EARLY IN THE MORNING IS A SMALL PRICE TO PAY TO AVOID WORLD WAR THREE BY KEEPING AN EYE ON A KINGMAKER IN A MADISON AVE. 'SINCERE' NECKTIE!

6/29 Copyright 1957, Field Enterprises, Inc. Registered U S Patent Office

MY PRINCESS, THE MAN CANYON AND THE MAN HOGAN MEET BY CHANCE UPON THE CURBSIDE!

THEY ARE HERE ALREADY, AMAH? IT IS HARDLY FIRST LIGHT—AND I MUST BEGIN TO ACT AS A QUEEN IN EXILE!

MILTON CANIFF

YOUR DESTINY IS BEYOND AVOIDANCE, MY PRINCESS! I DO NOT FATHOM THE MISTER HOGAN, BUT I SUPPORT HIM IN HIS EFFORT TO SUSTAIN YOUR POSITION!

BUT I DESIRE ONLY PEACE, NOT WAR AND TRAVAIL! I HAVE ALWAYS LOOKED WITH LONGING AT AMERICA! I WISH TO BE A PART OF ALL THIS!

THE TWO AMERICANS WALK AWAY TOGETHER DOWN THE STREET! THEY SPEAK IN WHAT MUST BE HOT WORDS!

BUT THEY WILL RE-TURN! MEANWHILE, I MAY SIT FOR A LITTLE TIME AND WATCH THE PEOPLE GOING SOURLY TO THE EVERYDAY WORLD I WISH I MIGHT SHARE!

STEVE CANYON

HOGAN, YOU UNDERSTAND, DON'T YOU, THAT IF PRINCESS SNOWFLOWER WERE IN THE UNITED STATES AS AN INVITED HEAD OF STATE, HER ACTIONS WOULD HAVE TO FOLLOW DIPLOMATIC PROTOCOL

OF COURSE, CANYON! — WHICH IS EXACTLY WHY I HAD HER ENTER THE COUNTRY AS A TOURIST!

IT WILL BE 'DISCOVERED' THAT SHE IS HERE INCOGNITO! SHE WILL RELUCTANTLY COME OUT OF HIDING WHEN HER FOLLOWERS DEMAND IT!

THEN IT WILL BE 'DISCOVERED' THAT SHE IS SEEKING MONEY TO GO HOME AND FIGHT THE REDS!

THERE WILL BE A 'SPONTANEOUS' MOVEMENT TO RAISE FUNDS TO SEND A VOLUNTEER ARMY BACK INTO CHINA —

— UNDER COMMAND OF PRINCESS SNOWFLOWER

OF COURSE THIS 'DISCOVERY' OF THE PRINCESS WILL MEAN THAT THE WHITE HOUSE MUST MAKE SOME SORT OF GESTURE! THEN THE MONEY WILL REALLY ROLL IN!

WHEN WE TAKE CHINA FROM THE REDS, SNOWFLOWER COULD BECOME THE RULER OVER THE ENTIRE COUNTRY!

LOOK, HOGAN, THE UNITED STATES RECOGNIZES THE PRINCESS AS THE EXILED HEAD OF WHAT WAS ONCE A FRIENDLY STATE—

BUT IF YOU USE HER TO FINANCE A WILDCAT REINVASION OF CHINA YOU'LL HAVE WORLD WAR THREE BLAMED ON HER!

WHAT'S IT TO YOU?

I AM ASSIGNED TO LOOK AFTER THE PRINCESS WHILE SHE IS HERE...

WELL, LOOK AFTER HER! SHOW HER THE TOWN!

KEEP HER FROM BEING HIT BY A TAXI!... BUY HER SOME POSTCARDS...

BUT DON'T STAND IN OUR WAY, EAGLE BEAGLE! WE'RE ALREADY IN BUSINESS...

— OUR FIRST CONTRIBUTION IS SOME FAST URANIUM MONEY FROM YOUR OLD CHUM...HAPPY EASTER!

...AND IF YOU TRY TO STOP IT— I'LL TELL YOUR BOSS BIRDMAN THAT YOU MADE A PASS AT THE ROYAL GUEST— AND YOU'LL BE IN CHARGE OF THE RESERVE SKY-HOOK REPAIR SQUADRON ON A DETACHED ICE FLOE OFF LITTLE AMERICA! — IF YOU'RE LUCKY!

GEE WHIZ! I'M SCARED STIFF!

6-30

162

CANYON, MY COMMON SENSE TELLS ME TO GET YOU OUT OF OUR HAIR, BUT WE DO NEED A DEVOTED WATCHDOG FOR PRINCESS SNOW-FLOWER

YOU'RE JUST DUMB AND LOYAL ENOUGH TO BE USEFUL IF WE RUN INTO TROUBLE!

HOGAN, YOU HAVE TOUCHED MY TENDER SENSIBILITIES! I SHALL STAY ON THE JOB, NOT BECAUSE THAT'S HOW MY ORDERS READ BUT BECAUSE YOU ARE SO FOLKSY!

I HAVE A DATE WITH SOME MOVIE PEOPLE!

GO EARN YOUR FLYING PAY BY TELLING THE PRINCESS HOW YOU WON WORLD WAR II SINGLE-HANDED!

OR DO THEY CALL IT 'LYING' PAY IN THEIR MORE HONEST MOMENTS IN THE AIR FORCE?

DON'T GET CAUGHT BY A TELEVISION CASTING DIRECTOR —REMEMBER WHAT HAS HAPPENED TO THE OTHER BIG COMEDIANS!

MR. HOGAN, MY CLIENT, AS YOU KNOW, IS A BIG NAME IN PICTURES, BUT SHE IS ALSO FAMOUS FOR HER SPONSORSHIP OF GOOD CAUSES...

OUR PUBLICITY PEOPLE HAVE LEARNED THAT A PRINCESS SNOWFLOWER, HEAD OF A SMALL STATE NOW OCCUPIED BY THE CHINESE REDS, IS IN THE U.S. AS A TOURIST — AND THAT YOU REPRESENT HER..

WE ALSO LEARNED THAT YOU HOPE TO RAISE FUNDS FOR A RE-INVASION OF CHINA FROM THE WEST! MY CLIENT BELIEVES WHOLE-HEARTEDLY IN YOUR CAUSE — AND WOULD LIKE TO PUBLICLY SPONSOR THE PRINCESS AND YOUR PROJECT...

I AM CERTAIN THE PRINCESS WILL BE DEEPLY MOVED BY YOUR CLIENT'S GENEROUS OFFER....

THERE IS JUST ONE LITTLE CONSIDERATION MY CLIENT WOULD ASK IN RETURN FOR THIS APPROBATION...

I DON'T KNOW TO WHAT I MAY COMMIT PRINCESS SNOWFLOWER! AS YOU KNOW, SHE ESCAPED FROM THE CHINESE REDS WITH ONLY THE CLOTHING SHE WORE...

MY CLIENT WISHES NOTHING FROM THE PRINCESS — EXCEPT AN AGREEMENT THAT SHE HAVE OFFICIAL PERMISSION TO MAKE A PICTURE BASED ON SNOWFLOWER'S LIFE!

YOU CAN UNDERSTAND HOW THIS WOULD CONFOUND AND CONFUSE THE PRINCESS... PERHAPS I CAN EXPLAIN IT TO HER — AND GET AN ANSWER FOR YOU...

LESSEE — WHEN WE HEAR FROM TWO MORE PHILANTHROPIC-PATRIOTIC FEMALE STARS WHO WILL MERELY WANT TO FILM THE PRINCESS' LIFE IN RETURN FOR PUBLIC SUPPORT, THEN I'LL CLOSE THE LIST—

...AND LET THE GIRLS FIGHT OVER THE PART UNTIL THE MOVIE COLUMNISTS HAVE TIME TO DRILL THE WORD INTO THE PUBLIC MIND!

MILTON CANIFF

CANYON, IT IS A PLEASURE TO WALK OUT WITH YOU! I CAN RELAX...

WELL, THANK YOU, PRINCESS! WOULD IT DISTURB YOU TO TALK ABOUT DR SHU?

WHEN THE REDS FINALLY CLOSED IN ON US, HOGAN CONVINCED ME THAT I COULD DO MY PEOPLE THE GREATEST GOOD BY SETTING UP A GOVERNMENT IN EXILE..

BUT DR. SHU SAID HIS PLACE WAS WITH THE SICK AND WOUNDED — SO HE BECAME A PRISONER OF THE COMMUNISTS... I NEVER HEARD FROM HIM AGAIN...

ARE YOU CERTAIN HE IS A PRISONER?

WHY SHOULD I HAVE ANY REASON TO DOUBT WHAT HOGAN TOLD ME?

NO REASON! NO REASON AT ALL...

MILTON CANIFF

7

168

169

170

STEVE CANYON

by MILTON CANIFF

LADIES AND GENTLEMEN, YOU ALL KNOW WHY WE ARE HERE — TO MEET THE WOMAN WHO SYMBOLIZES OUR HOPE OF INVADING RED CHINA FROM THE WEST...

PRINCESS SNOWFLOWER!

CANYON, IF YOU CRAB THIS ACT I'LL BREAK YOUR HEAD!

HOGAN, I WOULDN'T MISS IT FOR THE WORLD — INCLUDING THE SPEECH YOU WROTE FOR HER

MY DEAR AMERICAN FRIENDS: THERE WAS ONLY COLD FURY IN MY HEART WHEN I ESCAPED FROM THE RED HORDE, BUT TODAY I AM WARMED BY THE THOUGHT THAT SO MANY OF YOU KNOW AND CARE ABOUT MY EFFORTS TO DRIVE THE GODLESS MINIONS OF THE SOVIET FROM MY HOME...

...WHILE I REJOICE AT YOUR FAITH IN ME, I AM SADDENED AGAIN BY THE CERTAIN KNOWLEDGE THAT — IF AMERICA WERE TO BE OVERRUN AS WAS MY SMALL KINGDOM, THE CREATIVE PEOPLE — WRITERS, ARTISTS, ACTORS AND ALL OF YOU WHO SWAY PUBLIC OPINION — WOULD BE THE FIRST TO FACE A FIRING SQUAD!

7-14

7-21

178

THERE'S CANYON!

HE'S GOT THE GIRL!

BREAK OUT THE PULMOTOR!

AS THE POLICE START TO WORK ON THE LIMP FIGURE OF THE PRINCESS, STEVE GOES DOWN AGAIN WITH A WATERPROOF ELECTRIC TORCH...

...BUT THE 'BODY' HE IS LOOKING FOR IS AT THIS MOMENT CRAWLING FROM THE RESERVOIR AT A POINT SAFELY AWAY FROM THE BRIGHT SCENE!

THE PRINCESS WAS SEVERELY SHAKEN, BUT NOT SERIOUSLY HURT... A U.S. AIR FORCE LIEUT. COLONEL NAMED CANYON, WHO FOUGHT OFF THE ASSAILANTS, WAS TREATED FOR CUTS AND BRUISES... POLICE SAY...

...THE THREE MEN ESCAPED, BUT A ROUNDUP OF KNOWN COMMUNISTS IN THE AREA HAS BEGUN, SINCE THE PRINCESS IS ENGAGED IN AN EFFORT TO RE-INVADE CHINA FROM THE WEST...

"WASHINGTON OFFICIALS HAD NO COMMENT ON THE ATTACK EXCEPT TO EXPRESS SYMPATHY AND CONCERN FOR THE WELFARE OF THE HEAD OF A FRIENDLY GOVERNMENT..."

POOR STEVE

SIR, DID YOU SEE--

I'M SORRY TO SAY— I SAW IT! ....GET CANYON ON THE PHONE! HE DID A GOOD JOB OF PROTECTING THAT PRINCESS, BUT A POOR ONE OF KEEPING HER OFF THE FRONT PAGES!

WELL, COMRADE, YOU PUBLICITY-HAPPY HOLLYWOOD SLOBS SUCCEEDED IN MAKING A MARTYR OF THAT PRINCESS SNOWFLOWER! NEW YORK WANTS AN EXPLANATION—QUICK!

COMRADE! COMRADE! YOU MUST BELIEVE ME! WE HAD NOTHING TO DO WITH THAT ATTACK!

GREAT CIRCLE

7-28

183

7/31

THE POLICEMEN HAVE BEEN <u>SO</u> NICE TO ME!

THERE THEY ARE!

DON'T SMILE, PRINCESS! THIS IS GRIM BUSINESS!

WILL YOU MOVE IN BESIDE HER, MISTER?

NO—GET HER WITH THE D.A. AND COL. CANYON OF THE AIR FORCE—WHO PROTECTED HER!

THAT PICTURE WILL HIT EVERY NEWSPAPER AND TELEVISION NEWS-REEL IN THE COUNTRY!

CANYON, I CAN JUST SEE THE FACES ON YOUR STATE DEPARTMENT CHUMS WHEN IT APPEARS!

YOU MIGHT HAVE HAD ENOUGH CONSIDERATION FOR THE PRINCESS TO WEAR YOUR AIR FORCE UNIFORM TO BE PHOTOGRAPHED WITH HER WHEN IT WOULD DO HER SOME <u>REAL</u> GOOD!

8/1

MR. HOGAN, WE'RE SO HAPPY THE PRINCESS WAS ONLY SHAKEN UP BY HER EXPERIENCE—

BUT THE PUBLICITY VALUE WILL BE PRICE-LESS IN THE CITIES YOU WILL VISIT!

MM-HMM

BUT WE HAVE ALREADY HAD INQUIRIES FROM VARIOUS SOURCES RE-GARDING THE FEE THAT WILL BE PAID THE PRIN-CESS FOR HER PERSONAL APPEARANCES...

YOU WANT TO BE OFF THE HOOK IN CASE SNOWFLOWER TURNS OUT TO BE A PHONY. IS THAT IT?

WE WILL DONATE OUR EN-TIRE HONORARIUM, MINUS ACTUAL TRAVEL EXPENSES, TO THE RED CROSS—PRO-VIDED THAT <u>YOU</u> <u>DO</u> <u>THE</u> <u>SAME!</u>

IF I COULD ONLY STILL BE BOOKING ANIMAL ACTS IN VAUDEVILLE! FINK'S MULES DIDN'T BLACKMAIL AN AGENT INTO MAKING DONATIONS!

STEVE CANYON

by MILTON CANIFF

A HOTEL SUITE IN A SOUTHWESTERN CITY

NOW WE'RE IN BUSINESS! THAT ATTACK ON THE PRINCESS DID THE TRICK! THE PAPERS HERE ARE FULL OF BUILD-UP FOR SNOWFLOWER'S LOCAL APPEARANCE!

THEY ALSO QUOTE THE KNOWN COMMIES WHO WERE PICKED UP BY THE POLICE—

—THE REDS RATHER LOGICALLY HOLLERED, "WHY SHOULD WE BEAT HER UP AND MAKE A MARTYR OF HER BEFORE THE NORTH AMERICAN PUBLIC?"

SURE! SURE! —PRINCESS!.. YOU SPEAK AT THE WOMEN'S CLUB IN A FEW MINUTES!

HOGAN— I—I'M TIRED...

OF COURSE, PRINCESS! —YOU CAN REST ON THE PLANE TONIGHT!

HER FACE IS FLUSHED —SHE MUST BE RUNNING A FEVER!

I HAVE SOME ENERGY PILLS, PRINCESS... JUST TAKE THIS! THE ESCORT COMMITTEE IS DUE HERE ANY MINUTE...

HOLD IT, HOGAN! THIS CALLS FOR A DOCTOR'S DIAGNOSIS! THE GOOD LADIES CAN WAIT...

8-4

187

190

8-11

192

8/12 CANYON, YOUR ASSIGNMENT WAS TO KEEP PRINCESS SNOWFLOWER OUT OF THE PUBLIC EYE — BUT SHE HAS BEEN IN THE NEWSPAPERS AND TV NEWSREELS EVERY DAY!

SIR, SHE IS BEING ADVISED AND MANAGED BY A SHREWD OPERATOR NAMED HOGAN...

SINCE THEY HAVE NOT INCITED TO RIOT OR ADVOCATED THE OVERTHROW OF THE U.S. GOVERNMENT BY FORCE AND VIOLENCE, THEY HAVE A RIGHT TO SAY WHAT THEY CHOOSE...HAVEN'T THEY?

YOU KNOW WE MUST TREAT THE HEAD OF A FRIENDLY FOREIGN POWER WITH KID GLOVES!

TELEPHONE

IF WE TRY TO STOP SNOWFLOWER'S COUNTER-INVASION OF WESTERN RED CHINA, HOGAN THREATENS TO YELL 'COMMUNISTS IN THE STATE DEPARTMENT'...

— NOW, NOW, SIR! DON'T GO BACK TO YOUR LAW PRACTICE IN NEW YORK JUST YET! THIS MAY WORK ITSELF OUT-SOMEHOW!

8/13 AH, PRINCESS, THERE WILL BE BIG MONEY FOR YOUR CAMPAIGN IN THIS CITY! — DO YOU RECOGNIZE THE NAME?

HOGAN, I-I AM SORRY — I DID NOT NOTICE THE SIGN...I WISH ONLY TO SLEEP!

HEY, CAMPFIRE BOY CANYON, MAKE YOURSELF USEFUL FOR ONCE! TAKE THE PRINCESS AND THE OLD ONE TO THEIR HOTEL WHILE I MEET THE LOCAL DOUGH-BOYS!

YES, MAHSTUH!

PRINCESS SNOWFLOWER LISTLESSLY FOLLOWS STEVE TO THE BAGGAGE CLAIM AREA...THEN, SUDDENLY, HER HEAD SNAPS UP...

..AS SHE SEES A CHARTER CARGO PLANE UNLOADING ACROSS THE RAMP...

PRINCESS!

AT THIS MOMENT THE PEOPLE WHO HAVE BEEN UNLOADING HORSES FROM A CHARTER PLANE SEE THE PRINCESS AND...

THEY'RE MEN FROM MARS!

THE ROOSHINS HAVE ATTACKED WITH CAVALRY!

SEND THE RIOT SQUAD TO THE AIR-PORT! **QUICK!**

NO! NO! —THEY'RE FIRING BLANKS!

THOSE MEN ARE HARMLESS! I KNOW THEM! THEY ARE PRINCESS SNOWFLOWER'S SUBJECTS!

PRINCESSES, IS IT? SUBJECTS, IS IT? — AN' HE KNOWS 'EM YET! HE MUST BE ONE O' THEM UNDER— GROUNDER SUBVERSIFIERS! ARREST HIM BEFORE WE'RE ALL MURDERED IN OUR BEDS!

STEVE CANYON

by MILTON CANIFF

AS THEY NEAR THE EAST COAST, PRINCESS SNOW-FLOWER AND HOGAN ARE BECOMING MORE AND MORE THE SYMBOLS OF RE-INVASION OF WESTERN RED CHINA

LOOK! PRINCESS SNOWFLOWER DOLLS!

AND SNOWFLOWER HAIR STYLES IN THE BEAUTY SHOPS...

NOW WE'RE STARTING TO HIT IN NEWS-PAPER COLUMNS! CEDRIC ADAMS IN MINNE-APOLIS, HERB CAEN IN SAN FRANCISCO, MIKE CONNOLLY IN HOLLYWOOD, BILL GOLD IN WASHINGTON, JOHNNY JONES IN COLUMBUS AND IRV KUPCINET IN CHICAGO! — MAN, WE'RE ROLLING!

IT'S BEEN NICE TO HAVE YOU AROUND, STEVIEKINS...

...AND YOU HAVE NOT SLOWED US DOWN ONE BIT!

196

BY THE TIME WE HIT PHILADELPHIA, NEW YORK AND BOSTON WE'LL BE BIG RICH

...THEN WE CAN START TO RE-CRUIT!

THERE ARE ENOUGH EX-MILITARY PILOTS AROUND WHO ARE FED UP WITH CIVILIAN JOBS, TO GIVE US A STRIKING FORCE!

THE GROUND FORCE WE CAN GET TO LATER, AS LONG AS WE HAVE QUALITY OFFICERS AND NON-COMS!

THE EX-STAFF OF THE BRITISH INDIAN ARMY WOULD DO FOR A STARTER! WHEN YOU HAVE DOUGH YOU CAN DO ANY-THING!

ISN'T THAT RIGHT, BIRD-BOY CANYON?

NO COMMENT!

STATE DEPT.

WASHINGTON

FAR EAST.G.

AIR RAID

AH...GENERAL, I HAVE JUST COME FROM A MEETING ON THE PRINCESS SNOWFLOWER CASE... NOW ABOUT THAT LT. COL. CANYON YOU ASSIGNED TO LOOK AFTER HER...

SORRY IT DIDN'T WORK OUT! I'LL TAKE CANYON OFF THE JOB AT ONCE!

8-18

197

Copyright 1957, Field Enterprises, Inc. Registered U.S. Patent Office.

HAROLD, I JUST HAD A CALL FROM THE STATE DEPARTMENT...

IT WAS ABOUT THAT LIGHT COLONEL CANYON WE LENT THEM FOR A DETACHED DUTY JOB... DO YOU RECALL?

MILTON CANIFF

OH, YES, SIR! A FARSIGHTED AND SHREWD MOVE BY THE STATE PEOPLE IN SUCH A DELICATE SITUATION...

I'M GLAD YOU APPROVE

... BECAUSE THEY ASKED ME TO FIRE CANYON FOR FAILING TO KEEP THE GIRL OUT OF THE PUBLIC EYE!

WHY, THOSE PIN-WITTED HANDKISSERS IN STRIPED PANTS — WHAT RIGHT HAVE THEY TO TREAT AN AIR FORCE OFFICER THAT WAY?

Copyright 1957, Field Enterprises, Inc. Registered U.S. Patent Office.

TELEGRAM, COL. CANYON

1311

THANK YOU

"YOU ARE RELIEVED OF PRESENT DETACHED DUTY ASSIGNMENT AS OF ARRIVAL OF REPLACEMENT! REPORT THIS OFFICE WITH WRITTEN REPORT COVERING CASE TO DATE! WRITTEN ORDERS FOLLOW BY MAIL"

MILTON CANIFF

KNOCK

KNOCK

COL. CANYON, I AM ROSS OF THE STATE DEPARTMENT. I --

COME IN, MR. ROSS! THE TIMING IS GOOD! — FORTUNATELY, DEATH OCCURRED SLIGHTLY BEFORE THE UNDERTAKER ARRIVED!

199

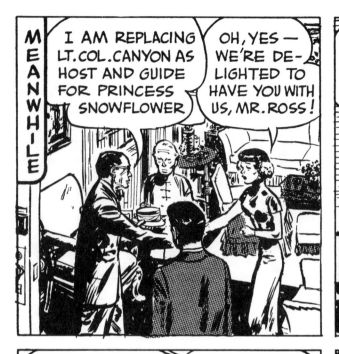

8-25

204

WHILE THE REPORTER IS RETURNING TO THE WESTERN CHINA BORDER AREA, STEVE WATCHES SNOWFLOWER AND HOGAN RISING IN THE PUBLIC EYE! — THEN HE GETS A CABLE FROM HIS FOREIGN CORRESPONDENT FRIEND...

9-I

207

209

9-8

212

PLEASE REGISTER MR. HOGAN INTO MY ROOM—HE HAD ONE TOO MANY TRANQUILIZER PILLS!

9-15

WH—WHAT'S THIS, COL. CANYON?

JUST WHAT I SAID = PUT MY ROOM ON DOUBLE INSTEAD OF SINGLE RATE! — MR. HOGAN WILL SIGN THE REGISTER WHEN HE RETURNS FROM OUTER SPACE!

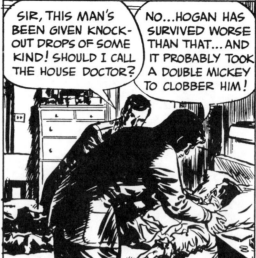

SIR, THIS MAN'S BEEN GIVEN KNOCK-OUT DROPS OF SOME KIND! SHOULD I CALL THE HOUSE DOCTOR?

NO...HOGAN HAS SURVIVED WORSE THAN THAT... AND IT PROBABLY TOOK A DOUBLE MICKEY TO CLOBBER HIM!

WHAT WAS HIS TROUBLE—A WOMAN, MONEY, AMBITION—OR JUST PLAIN CUSSEDNESS?

ALL OF THEM—IN ONE DAY! EVEN THE MEN WHO STOOD UNDER THE AIR-TO-AIR ATOMIC ROCKET BURST COULDN'T HAVE HELD UP UNDER SO MUCH PRESSURE!

WONDER WHAT HOGAN IS DREAMING ABOUT—THE STUBBORN MUGG...

...HE'S THE SORT OF TOUGH JOKER WHO WINS HERO MEDALS—THEN CAN'T ADJUST TO PEACE! ...HE ALWAYS HAS TO BE FIGHTING WITH SOMEONE!

HE PROBABLY REALLY BELIEVED HE COULD INVADE WESTERN CHINA AND PUT PRINCESS SNOWFLOWER BACK ON HER THRONE!...

I'M SURE HE DIDN'T EVEN THINK ONCE THAT HE COULD TRIGGER WORLD WAR III AND START THE KILLING OF A FEW MILLION PEOPLE!

WELL—GOTTA GET TO SLEEP... THE ADVENTURES OF PRINCESS SNOWFLOWER ARE CATCHING UP WITH ME!

...AS STEVE GOES TO BRUSH HIS TEETH, HOGAN STIRS—AND OPENS HIS EYES...

WHEN STEVE WAKES UP THE MORNING AFTER SAVING HOGAN FROM THE MUGGERS, DOAGIE HAS DEPARTED—AND THE ONLY FAREWELL MESSAGE IS A CHINESE PHRASE — TRACED IN SHAVING CREAM ON THE BATHROOM MIRROR...

...ROUGHLY TRANSLATED—IT MEANS "NUTS TO YOU"!

HASTILY STEVE MAKES A CALL TO THE BANK WHERE CONTRIBUTIONS TO SNOW-FLOWER'S CAMPAIGN WERE DEPOSITED

WHY, I PRESUME, COL. CANYON, THAT THE PRINCESS WILL HAVE THE FUNDS RETURNED TO THE DONERS...

THE SUM IS INTACT!.. MR. HOGAN NEVER WITHDREW A PENNY FOR HIMSELF!

NOW WE SKIP BACK IN TIME TO THE PERIOD WHEN STORIES OF STEVE AND THE PRINCESS WERE NEWS ALL OVER THE COUNTRY...

GEE..

...AS HER CAMPAIGN TO RE-INVADE RED CHINA FROM THE WEST GAINS MOMENTUM, PRINCESS SNOWFLOWER AND HER CONSTANT ESCORT LT. COL. CANYON OF THE U.S. AIR FORCE WERE RIVAL ATTRACTIONS TO THE BASE-BALL TEAM IN MILWAUKEE...

OF ALL THE PLUSH ASSIGNMENTS! THAT CANYON MUST REALLY KNOW WHERE THE BODY IS BURIED UNDER THE PENTAGON

NOTHING ELSE TO DO BUT SQUIRE THAT CUTE CHINA DOLL AROUND THE COUNTRY!

THIS WENT ON FOR QUITE AWHILE... —THEN ONE DAY...

TORRY, DOES POTEET EAT AT THE BX OR THE SNACK BAR ON THE BASE!

I DUNNO, MADGE! GUESS I NEVER NOTICED! —WHY?

FOR NEARLY A WEEK NOW SHE HAS HAD SOME EXCUSE NOT TO EAT AT MEALTIME...

MAYBE IT'S JUST TOO HOT!

COME IN, MRS. TORR... WHAT CAN WE DO FOR A HEALTHY GAL LIKE YOU?

IT'S ABOUT POTEET CANYON, DOCTOR! LET ME TELL YOU THE STORY...

THE PSYCHIATRISTS HAVE TREATMENTS FOR ANOREXIA NERVOSA—WHICH IS SIMPLY LACK OF APPETITE RESULTING FROM NERVOUS TENSIONS...

BUT LET'S TRY ONE CLOSER TO HOME! MY SON IS A FRESHMAN AT THE STATE UNIVERSITY—AND THEY HAVE THEIR FIRST FOOTBALL WEEKEND COMING UP...

9-22

STEVE CANYON
WILL RETURN IN
"WARGAMES"